HENRY FORD'S AIRPORT
and
Other Aviation Interests
1909 - 1954

TIMOTHY J. O'CALLAGHAN

Proctor Publications of Ann Arbor

PRINTED IN THE UNITED STATES OF AMERICA

STOUT METAL AIRPLANE COMPANY

DIVISION OF
FORD MOTOR COMPANY
DEARBORN, MICHIGAN

Ford Motor Company

STOUT METAL AIRPLANE DIVISION

DEARBORN, MICHIGAN

PREFACE

Much has been written about Henry Ford, the Ford Tri-Motor airplane and many other facets of the world wide operations of the Ford Motor Company, and while references concerning the Ford Airport and other aviation related activities have been mentioned in many of these articles and books, they were always fragmentary. The author always had other points he was trying to make and comments about Ford aviation were usually casual and always left me wanting to know just a little bit more. Hopefully this will be a case of "everything you will ever want to know about Ford in aviation."

My interest in Ford history came through my father's 25 years and my 40 years with the Ford and Lincoln Mercury Sales Divisions of Ford Motor Company. As my family grew older and left the nest, I found I had time and money to start collecting Ford memorabilia and this very quickly led to an interest in the Ford Tri-Motor airplane. Several things happened in the mid 1980's to intensify this interest. First was my acquaintance with Bill Larkins, author of The Ford Story, published in 1957 and The Ford Tri-Motor 1926 - 1992, published in 1992. As all airplane buffs know, Bill's books are the bible on the Ford Tri-Motor airplane and I have been fortunate to exchange many letters with him over the years and had the pleasure of visiting with him in his California home. He was a constant source of information and encouragement. Second, after trying in vain for a number of years to get a ride in a Ford plane, in August 1990, Paul Poberenzy, founder of the Experimental Aircraft Association, Oshkosh, WI, was kind enough to roll out their rebuilt Ford, 4AT69, and take me for a flight around the city as "Co-pilot." What a thrill! Third, I acquired the Ford aviation photographic files from the Aeronautical Archives in the estate of Steve Hudek, amounting to over 2000 prints and negatives. Many of these were copied, with the permission of the Ford Motor Company, from the original photographs in their archives. Fourth and last, I have been able to review all of the 50,000 plus prints and negatives, and all files relating to Ford Motor Company's Airplane Division in the Research Center, Henry Ford Museum & Greenfield Village, as well as related files in the Dearborn Historical Society and the Stanley Knauss papers in the Burton Historical Society files in the Detroit Public Library. As I live in the Detroit area I have been able to methodically review this material over a period of time which has led me to many prints, negatives and records which haven't been seen in years and some which have never been seen by persons interested in Ford aviation. As a result of my research, I have been able to blend scattered information, that was previously known, with a great deal of detail recently found in the files.

I have kept my comments on the 4AT and 5AT Tri-Motors to a minimum, as I look on this effort as a companion piece to Bill Larkins' book which is required reading for anyone with a greater interest in these planes.

I owe a big debt of gratitude to Cynthia Reid-Miller and other members of the Research Center of the Henry Ford Museum & Greenfield Village for all of their advice and the many trips they made to the "stacks" so I could look for just one more bit of information, and to Darleen Flaherty of the Ford Industrial Archives. To Sam Sturgis and John Bluth, contributors and fellow Ford aviation enthusiasts. And finally, to my wife for finding the spelling and grammatical errors the rest of us missed.

Henry Ford Museum refers in all cases to The Henry Ford Museum & Greenfield Village. An FMC number on photographs indicates the original Ford Motor Company negative number. Copies can be obtained from the Henry Ford Museum.

This, my first book, I dedicate to the ladies in my life; Doris, my wife and Patricia, my daughter.

1

INTO AVIATION

Van Auken's plane with a Ford Model "T" engine in 1909. Ford's first aviation venture. (Henry Ford Museum FMC O.335)

Ford's Earliest Venture

Henry Ford's first venture into aviation came in 1909 when Charles Van Auken, an office employee of Ford's, persuaded him to finance the building of a Bleriot type airplane powered by a 28hp model T engine. He was assisted by C. J. Smith who, with Harold Hicks in 1926, de- signed and patented the first tail wheel for an airplane. Parts were made by Ford employees and the total cost was $985. Edsel Ford has been credited with assisting in the design and build- ing of this plane, but in a biographical sketch provided to the National Aeronautic Association in 1929 he merely states **"(I) Became interested in aviation in 1910, when (a) plane was built by Ford Motor Company with (a) Model "T" engine for power."** The plane was first flown from a Ford owned farm on what is now the Dearborn Country Club, but the engine was insufficient to properly power the flight. Even after extensive reworking of the engine, the power to weight ratio was never adequate to get it more than six feet off the ground and it finally crashed into a tree on the Fort Wayne (Detroit) parade ground, slightly injuring Van Auken and temporarily ending Henry Ford's interest in aviation.

Ford's Renewed Interest

Ford's renewed interest in aviation was fueled by the development of the airship as a passenger carrying vehicle. The *Army and Navy Journal* reported that Ford had proposed to the US Government, in the summer of 1919, to **"build an airship without a cent of money to be paid until the craft is finished and accepted."** They further reported on March 6, 1920 that William Mayo, Ford's Chief Engineer, speaking for Mr. Ford stated, **"that they stood ready to build a hangar to accommodate an airship 1,000 feet long, furnish all the necessary material and equipment, develop the engines for the craft, and build a dirigible without taking a cent of profit from the government."** Mayo further stated that, **"the Ford Company had a representative in Germany looking into the possibility of purchasing a German dirigible as a model or, failing that, to buy plans and hire experienced personnel to come to the US to produce them."** Ford's costs were estimated to run about a million dollars each for the prototype airship and a new facility for production. Ford's proposal encountered a marked difference of opinion between two Navy groups with one group wanting the Navy to do all the first building of an airship and the other group who was convinced that no progress would be made in the development of these airships without the involvement of private enterprise and capital. Ford sent Mayo to Europe in July 1920 to survey the aviation field and determine whether Ford should undertake construction of airships in the US, but nothing further came of these plans. However, the Fords' interest in aviation was still alive, for in 1922 Edsel Ford contributed $5,000 to be used as prize money for the National Airplane Races held at Selfridge airfield, Mt. Clemens, MI.

Henry Ford's final step in engaging actively in aviation was a direct outgrowth of Mayo's and Edsel Ford's involvement with William Stout, an extraordinary individual who had been active in aviation for many years. He was a pioneer in the United States in the use of the thick wing, braced internally (eliminating the need for all the struts, braces and guy wires then in use) and the use of all metal in planes in the US at a time when everything was made of wood frames covered by fabric. Stout, being well known in aviation circles, wrote letters to 87 leading Detroit industrialists in November 1922 in an effort to get their commitment to aviation. In early 1923, he requested $1,000 to

$5,000 each for the formation of a new airplane company to build the first all metal commercial airplane. He promised them only **"that you will never see your money again."** It was to be an investment in aviation and to help make

December 1923 Edsel Ford had joined this select group by sending his check for $2,000.

Stout formed the Stout All Metal Airplane Company in 1922 to develop the first commercial

Stout's Air Sedan was first all metal commercial airplane in the United States. Too small to be a commercial success and too expensive for personal use, it did prove the practicality of all metal construction. (Hudek)

Detroit the aviation center of the US, just as it was the center of the automotive industry. As a result of war profits and the fantastic growth of the automobile, there were a great many wealthy individuals in Detroit. By April of 1924 Stout had 62 subscribers and the list would eventually grow to 128. Four months earlier in

all metal airplane in the US, but aircraft designers were limited by the engines available and in the early 1920's World War I surplus engines were so abundant and inexpensive there was little incentive to develop new aviation engines. By early 1923 Stout had developed a small all metal plane called the Air Sedan. Powered by one of the surplus 90hp OX-5 engines, it proved to be too expensive for a private plane and too small to be commercially successful. But he had demonstrated the practicality of fabricating an all metal aircraft, however, and started work on a larger all metal plane. Financed by his successful solicitation of the Detroit businessmen, he developed the Air Pullman, named after the passenger railroad cars, which was an eight person, all metal monoplane powered by the war surplus 400hp Liberty engine. This Air Pullman, named the *Maiden Detroit* (i.e. Made In Detroit), was test flown April 23, 1924 at Selfridge airfield, Mt Clemens, MI 26 miles north of the Stout factory in Detroit. This first Stout 2AT was sold to the US Post Office in December 1924 for $25,000 as the result of a crash landing. On a trip from Dayton, OH to Detroit, MI, on October 5, 1924 the engine caught fire and in sideslipping to extinguish the blaze, the engine died, forcing a crash landing. Due to the minimal damage suffered by the plane and the fact that none of the *ten* occupants were injured, Professor Edward Warner, a Post Office aviation consultant who was on board, submitted such a favorable report that the Post Office decided to purchase it. By March of 1925, when the second plane was built in his new Dearborn factory at Ford Airport, it was designated an

Air Pullman and named the *Maiden Dearborn*. It was later designated an Air Transport 2AT as this was Stout's second commercial airplane and Ford would be using them in his Air Transport Service to transport freight rather than passengers.

The importance of all metal in the construction of airplanes was very clearly spelled out in Ford's 1927 airplane catalog:

"No one, no matter how skilled, can inspect a piece of wood and tell how strong it is. Spruce should stand 40,000 pounds pull per square inch; but no one, by examining it, can tell whether it will pull 40,000 pounds or fail at 25,000 pounds. Its flexibility, too, is an unknown quantity; no two pieces will flex alike under strain.

Metal, however, is a determinate: it is possible to estimate within 5 percent its strength."

Bill Stout made the point more succinctly when he remarked, **"Any plywood plane after six months time will start developing a 'veneereal disease.'"**

2

FORD AIRPORT

The Airfield

R. T. Walker, Mayo's secretary, claims to have drafted the March 21, 1923 letter that Stout sent to Mayo so that Edsel Ford would have something definite to discuss with his father, Henry Ford. The letter detailed the efforts Stout's organization had put forward, including the fact they had 34 people already pledged to contribute $1,000 to $5,000 and pleading for assistance in three areas:

"First: The moral and financial support of the community and its big men.

Second: A place to do our work well, with a flying field close at hand.

Third: A motor development, connected with our work that will enable us to have developed a cheap engine ready for production by a year from this coming summer."

Stout went on to state, **"The layout of your eight-cylinder radial should be an ideal one when developed."** (In October 1925 Ford did announce an X type air cooled engine to newsmen. While never developed beyond the prototype stage, it was an eight cylinder engine with four banks of two cylinders in tandem, set at right angles to each other and designed to develop 200 to 250hp.) Mayo passed the letter on to Edsel Ford stating:

"I believe that Mr. Stout's efforts have been of a high enough character to warrant giving him some assistance, either in cash, a free lease for a certain length of time of a piece of property, a free lease of some building we may not be using, or any other combination that might suggest itself to you."

In March 1924, after the first plane was completed, Stout complained about having to drag his plane 26 miles from his factory on Beaubien Street in Detroit to Selfridge airfield for testing and demonstration flights. The Fords, having watched the development and performance of the *Maiden Detroit* con-

Ford experimental eight cylinder aircraft engine with Hamilton propeller. Although there was much talk of Ford's aircraft engine, none were ever mass produced. (Henry Ford Museum, digital enhancement of FMC 189.3377)

cluded that Stout's ideas were practical. Henry Ford, believing that air transportation was to be as important as the automobile and that Stout's plane was the best available for a commercial application, agreed to build an airport and an airplane factory.

Three sites with adequate land, in the vicinity of the Ford Administration building in Dearborn, were proposed to Stout and by July 1924 the site bordered by Oakwood Boulevard, (what is now) Rotunda Drive and the Southfield Expressway was selected. When Stout decided it was the best of the locations, even though the most expensive to prepare, Henry Ford responded, **"That doesn't make any difference. If it will make the best field, that is the one we will take."** The land was planned for a housing subdivision and when Liebold, Ford's secretary, complained that

$15,000 had already been spent developing the site, Henry Ford replied, **"Maybe it was a subdivision yesterday, but today it is a landing field."** Ford put 40 tractors working to level the property for its new use and for nearly five months men were kept busy reshaping the landscape and moving 75,000 cubic feet of earth. Supervision of the construction of the airfield and airplane factory was turned over to Glen Hoppin, Stout's business manager, as Mayo claimed that he had no Ford executive available to handle this additional task. An early problem developed when the Michigan Central railroad refused to remove unused tracks to a Ford facility that ran directly across proposed runway number two, as the railroad feared they would lose their right of way. This was finally resolved by lowering the tracks twelve inches and covering them with dirt. The tracks remained until concrete runways were installed several years later.

The site for the airfield consisted of 719 acres

At dedication of Ford Airport, January 15, 1925. Left to right: William Mayo, Edsel Ford, Major Thomas Lamphier, Henry Ford, William Stout. In April 1943, Lamphier's son, Capt. Thomas Lamphier, participated in a secret Army Air Corps long distance flight that intercepted and shot down the airplane carrying Admiral Isoroku Yamamoto, planner of the Pearl Harbor raid. (Hudek)

Ford Airport June 1925. This was the most modern airport in the US! The Stout factory is at left center with the hangar at right center. The mooring mast is at the upper right. (Hudek FMC 1008.AP2153-B)

Ford Airport September 1926. The new factory, not yet occupied, is on the left. New concrete runways would not be started until April 1928. (Hudek FMC 189.3737)

Ford Airport August 1930. From left, enlarged airplane factory, new hangar, old hangar and terminal building. Concrete runways, the first in the world, were finished in the spring of 1929. (Hudek FMC 189.7653)

Ford Airport July 1931. Newly opened Dearborn Inn is on the left. Terminal building is in the foreground. (Henry Ford museum FMC 833.56304.9)

assembled from eight parcels Henry Ford had previously acquired for $485,385 (although they were later to be carried on the books of the Airplane Division for $1,624,176). 260 acres to the north were later set aside for what is now the Henry Ford Museum and Greenfield Village.

The airfield consisted of two grass runways which was typical of the period: number 1 runway (3,400 feet), running northeast to southwest and number 2 runway (3,700 feet, later extended to 4,200 feet), running northwest to southeast. Both were 75 feet wide. More than 20 miles of drain tiles were laid for year round operation and though not normally operated at night, the field was fully equipped with flood lights to accommodate night landings when necessary. To identify the airfield from the air the word **F O R D** was formed with white crushed stone 200 feet high and visible from 10,000 feet in the air. One of the many firsts for Ford Airport.

By November 1924 the field was completed and on November 15th the *New York Times* ran an article announcing the decision to call it **"Ford Airport"**. While Edward Hamilton in the *Maiden Detroit* was the first to land on November 16, 1924, the airport was not formally dedicated until January 15, 1925. The dedication ceremonies were highlighted by an aerial demonstration of 12 aircraft of the Army's First Pursuit Squadron from Selfridge airfield commanded by Major Thomas Lamphier. It was hailed by civil and military aviation authorities as the finest field in the United States and better than most airfields in the world. Martin Greif, in his The Airport Book, comments that it took a capitalist's money to create America's first international airport. Private civilian and military planes were made welcome anytime, free of charge.

At the same time, Ford was busy building a hangar and a factory and announced in the *Ford News* (an employee newspaper) for July 15, 1924, **"For the purpose of encouraging aircraft development the Ford interests will erect a modern factory building devoted to research in aviation. The buildings will be used by the Stout Metal Airplane Company and the Aircraft Development Corporation."** The Aircraft Development Corporation had been formed in 1922, with Edsel Ford, Bill Mayo and William Stout (among the many Detroit dignitaries) appointed as officers with the task of developing the first airship with an all metal gas envelope for commercial use. In 1929 they were to build the only metal clad rigid airship ever made, the ZMC-2 (Zeppelin Metal Clad, 2nd version) for the US Navy, at a factory on Grosse Ile, MI. It was a small stubby airship; 149 feet, 5 inches long with a displacement of 202,200 cubic feet, made of Alclad (the same material as the Ford Tri-Motor airplanes) and nicknamed the *Tin Bubble*. The Aircraft Development Corporation never utilized the Ford factory, although their name originally appeared on the building along with the Stout Metal Airplane Company. But in 1929, Ford airplane workers did fabricate the airship's gondola.

Records show that as early as March 1926, Major Schroeder, the Airport Manager, was proposing the use and layout of hard runways stating:

"I feel sure that as our planes get bigger and heavier it will take a very heavy tough sod to hold us up, particularly during the spring of the year or after heavy rains. We are already reducing our loads to 500 and 600 pounds in order to get out of the mud."

Indeed, after the first Air Tours in September 1925, some pilots were already calling it "Lake Ford." It was not until December 1927, however, that the *Ford News* announced that a 600 foot concrete runway was to be installed for testing purposes. By April 1928 a contract had been let to pave 1,800 feet of runway #2; 75 feet wide and 7 inches thick. By the end of 1928, 1,000 feet of runway # 1 was completed and the remaining 1,500 feet of #2 was paved in the Spring of 1929. The cost was $90,448 and the contractors had to buy reinforcing rods and cement from Ford. (As a comparison, the new runway at Metro Airport, Detroit, MI is 8,200 feet long, 150 feet wide and 17 inches thick.) The 1991 Smithsonian Air and Space book, <u>Aviation Milestones</u>, states, **"Henry Ford's greatest contribution to aviation was in building the first airport in the world with concrete**

Rudolph (Shorty) Schroeder, first Ford Airport manager as a World War I Army pilot . (Robert Baron)

runways." However, it was not always that obvious, for as late as 1940, John Wood in his book, <u>Airports</u>, a comprehensive study of the worlds major airports, commented **"It is quite possible that we are somewhat overdoing it in regard to the enormous areas of costly hard-surfaced runways that we are laboriously providing."**

Years later, Charles Lindbergh related the story Bill Mayo told of how he had tried to arrange with the airlines flying into Detroit to use Ford Airport as a terminal. One Sunday a large number of planes flew over the Ford house, which was close by the airfield, and Mrs. Ford told her husband that those planes oughtn't to be flying on Sunday. The next day, Henry Ford told Mayo to close the airport on Sundays. In addition, Ford had gotten word that visiting pilots were bringing liquor into the airport. Ford, a teetotaler, issued orders banning alcohol and this ban, added to the Sunday closing, drove many plane owners and pilots to the newly opened

City Airport in Detroit, effectively ending the possibility of Ford Airport being used as a terminal for commercial airlines.

Factory and Hangar

Bill Stout, in his book, So Away I Went, relates how, when Henry Ford told him to design his airplane factory, they decided the type of building and the rent:

"Awed at the expenditure of even small amounts on such a precarious thing as aviation, we designed the cheapest type

2AT-1 (*Maiden Detroit*) under construction in 1924 at the Stout Metal Airplane Company factory, Beaubien Street, Detroit, MI. (Hudek)

of steel and brick construction that would fit the need. Very shortly the building was put up and we were told to move in on a basis to be decided later."

Hoppin relates that Mayo directed the price be kept under $100,000, which probably accounts for Stout's claim that they designed the cheapest construction. Several months later Mayo advised them their rent would be $1,500 a year ($125 monthly). A very modest sum indeed considering they had been paying $500 a month on their Beaubien Street plant! Interestingly, the *Ford News* announced that the airplane factory had been donated to the Stout Company. The 20,000 square foot factory was occupied October 15, 1924.

A hangar and airport operations building, 65' x 120', equipped with a 6,000 gallon capacity gas tank for servicing Stout's, and visiting, planes was constructed near the new factory and occupied April 27, 1925. By July 1925 a large **Ford Airport** sign costing $1,085 was erected on top of this hangar facing Oakwood Boulevard. The letters, 4 to 5 feet high, were wood, painted gold, mounted on a mesh framework 44' x 12' 6". They were illuminated at night by eight flood lights.

The Airplane factory cost $71,516 and the hangar $44,176. Property improvements, mostly fencing and concrete, accounted for another $39,799.

Lt. Col. John Pagelow, commander of the Army's airship RS-1. Note Army Airship Pilot's wings on his chest. (Henry Ford Museum, segment of FMC 189.3719)

US Army airship *RS-1* was the first to dock at the Ford mooring mast , September 18, 1926. It was 284 feet long with a 755,500 cubic foot gas capacity. (Henry Ford Museum FMC 189.3697)

US Navy airship *Los Angeles* docked October 15, 1926. It was 650 feet long with a 2,475,000 cubic foot gas capacity. The *RS-1* and *Los Angeles* were only two airships to use the mooring mast. (Henry Ford Museum FMC 189.3787)

Henry Ford with Adm. William Moffett (left), head of the Navy's Bureau of Aeronautics and Lt. Cmdr. Charles Rosendahl, Commander of the airship *Los Angeles*. Adm. Moffett had introduced Richard Byrd to the Fords, leading to their backing of his polar expeditions. (Henry Ford Museum FMC 189.3765)

By July 1925 the airport was staffed by a manager, three pilots (L. Manning, E. Hamilton & W. DeWald), two assistant pilots (C. Sinclair & D. Burford), three mechanics (H. Russell, C. Bradley & H. West), two janitors and a clerk. Major Rudolph (Shorty) Schroeder (6'2") was appointed the first airport manager and chief test pilot. Schroeder had been the Army's chief test pilot at McCook Field, Dayton, OH and had set a world's altitude record of 33,114 feet in 1920. On November 6, 1926 he was abruptly replaced by Edward Hamilton, the senior Ford pilot. An *Aero Digest* article in December 1926 reported that Schroeder **"had his head lopped off due to the fact he differed in his estimates of the performance that could be expected of the Ford Tri-Motor, when**

only two of its three motors are working."

By November 1928 Hamilton had left Ford to fly for himself and was replaced by LeRoy Manning, another Ford pilot, who ran the airport operations until his death in the crash of the Ford experimental bomber XB906 on September 19, 1931. He was followed by Harry Russell, an Army pilot who had been hired as one of the original Ford airplane mechanics and who had, by January 1926, been promoted to pilot. He then worked his way up to senior pilot and won the 1930 and 1931 Ford Reliability Air Tours in a Ford Tri-Motor. After the Ford Airplane Division closed, Russell continued to work for Ford in a supervisory capacity retiring in January of 1968.

Dirigible Mooring Mast

The dirigible mooring mast (erected in 1925) has been attributed to the visit in October 1924 of Dr. Hugo Eckner, who had just delivered the airship ZR-3 (later rechristened the *Los Angeles*), to the United States Government as part of German World War I reparations.

"The next time you come to Detroit you should bring your airship with you," said Henry Ford.

"I'd like to," Dr. Eckner replied, **"but you have no mooring mast."**

Mr. Ford replied, **"That's easy. I'll build one."**

Unfortunately, the site for the mast happened to be right in the middle of what Liebold and the Wayne County Road Commission had agreed was to be a 204 foot wide super highway called Southfield Road. Once again Liebold had to change his plans. By June 1925 the Aircraft Development Corporation had designed, and had installed, at Ford Airport the largest, most modern and only privately owned mooring mast in the world. A unique feature of this mooring system allowed an airship, once fastened to the mast, to ride freely on a rotating collar so it could always face into the wind and allowed it to be lowered to the ground. This haul down device permitted cargo and ballast loading, repairs and passenger disembarkation at ground level. Previous systems required passengers to disembark through the bow of the ship and then be lowered to the ground in a small elevator. Either the haul down device wasn't designed to work in all weather conditions or the designers had reservations about its practicality as they also installed an elevator to the top in the center of the tower. In any event, Ford motion picture film reveals the haul down device was never used. The tower was a three legged steel structure 210 feet high with 72 feet between legs, designed to withstand 100 mile per hour winds. (Heaviest recorded velocity in the Detroit area had been 87 miles per hour.) Facilities at the tower included buoyant gas, gasoline, water, telephone and electric lights on the mast and it could accommodate airships of 10,000,000 cubic feet capacity. It was painted with alternate bands of chrome yellow, black and white giving it high visibility in clear weather as well as fog. It was planned that the Navy airship *Shenandoah* would be the first airship to dock there and in fact Lieutenant Commander Charles Rosendahl had wired Major Schroeder on September 2, 1925 that **"Department has authorized trip for Mr. Ford and Mr. Mayo to Bay City and return or to Lakehurst."** However, on September 4th, two days into her Midwest tour, she was destroyed in a storm near Ava, OH. It was a year later on September 18, 1926 that the Army airship *RS-1* (284 feet long, 755,500 cubic feet), Lieutenant Colonel John Pagelow commanding, became the first ship to use the mast. The *RS-1* was made by the Goodyear Zeppelin Corp., Akron, OH and driven by two propellers, each powered by a pair of the same World War I surplus Liberty engines used to power the Stout 2AT airplanes. The Navy's *Los Angeles* (650 feet long, 2,475,000 cubic feet), visited a month later on October 15, 1926. She was commanded by Lt. Cmdr. Charles Rosendahl who had been the navigator of the *Shenandoah* when she crashed the previous year and who would be the Commanding Officer of the Lakehurst Naval Air Station in NJ when the German airship *Hindenburg* exploded in flames in 1937. Promoted to Admiral, Rosendahl went on to command the Navy's blimp fleet on the Atlantic coast during World War II. These would be the only airships to dock at Ford Airport and the only two times the mooring mast was used. On October 23, 1926 Lt.

Cmdr. Wicks wrote, at Maj. Schroeder's request, a critique of Ford's mooring mast. His comments centered on inadequate field lights, winches with inadequate speed control for airship mooring and the unique haul down device previously described, which he states was a serious handicap. He was further concerned with availability of a fixed ground crew fully trained and available for mooring work. Lt. Cmdr. Wick's comments apparently jolted the Ford organization, for Mayo requested additional criticism of the mooring mast from Fred Lamkey, a former mooring master. In a letter dated November 10, 1926, Lamkey stated, **"the Ford Mooring Tower, though the latest, most expensive and finest looking, is inferior to any in the country."** He then went on to explain why, citing most of the same problems Lt. Cmdr. Wicks mentioned, particularly the haul down device.

Sperry Beacon

By July 1, 1925, a 450,000,000 candlepower Sperry Beacon, or searchlight (similar to those in use by the US Air Mail for night flying), was installed on the southeast corner of the hangar for **"airship maneuvers after dark and in fog."** Tests by the Airmail Service determined that it was visible for 100 miles at an altitude of 700 feet, and up to 130 miles under optimum conditions. In fact, the flashing beam was plainly visible at dusk on July 1, 1925 to the crowds at the dedication of the new Cleveland Municipal Airport over ninety miles away. It had a 36 inch diameter lens that produced more light than the headlights of all the 9,000,000 Ford cars then in operation and a beam so hot that it would burn paper several feet away. Its heat was described as **"the nearest approach to the density of the sun, yet to be produced."** It was three feet long and set to provide a continuous revolving beacon, but could be revolved and tilted through any angle.

Sperry Beacon, installed July 1925, produced more light than the headlights of the nine million Ford cars then on the road and could be seen eighty miles away in Lo-rain, OH. The *Maiden Dearborn II* is in background. (Henry Ford Museum FMC 189.2678)

3

FORD AIR TRANSPORT SERVICE

The First Scheduled Airline

In an attempt to further demonstrate the safety and commercial viability of air transport, Ford launched his own Air Transport Service on April 13, 1925 to carry freight and company mail between Dearborn and Maywood Field near Chicago, IL. This first flight was made

Mechanic Harry Russell and Pilot Eddie Hamilton ready to inaugurate the Ford Air Transport Service between Detroit and Chicago on April 13, 1925. Both would become Ford Airport managers. (Henry Ford Museum FMC 833.41670)

Stout 2AT-2 *Maiden Dearborn* at Ford Airport. First of the Stout planes to be used in the Ford Air Transport Service. (Hudek FMC 833.42449)

in the 2AT-2 *Maiden Dearborn* piloted by Edward Hamilton with Harry Russell as flight mechanic. On April 19, 1925 the *New York Times* ran an article on Ford's aviation activities titled, **"Ford Prepares To Develop Flying Flivver,"** one of the first uses of the Flivver name in relation to Ford aircraft. In the same article the Times stated, **"The company mail between those branches (Chicago and Detroit) averages 800 pounds, or 32,000 letters a day, each way. Each plane saves $1,250 a day in postage."** Considering the fact that only one plane was in operation and the statement was based on about four day's activity, this is an incredibly exaggerated statement. Just ten months later Ford would carry only 249 pounds of US

mail, highly inflated by collectors covers, on both legs of the highly publicized inaugural United States Air Mail flights to both Chicago and Cleveland. Yet these figures keep being repeated in articles on Ford aviation. With the addition of a Cleveland route on July 1, 1925 the pilots flew round trips on alternate days as it was felt it would not be safe for them to make daily round trip flights. Safety was a major concern, quoting Mayo: **"In as much as the venture is a new one with us and as the eyes of the whole world are centered on us, we are trying to use every precaution to make all our moves in the air a decided success."** On their off days, the pilots were subject to call at any time and were required to report to Maj. Schroeder at least three times a day. Ground was broken for a new Ford hangar in Cleveland, designed by noted architect Albert Kahn, in February 1926 and was occupied in June of the same year. In 1926 Maywood Field, under government control, was 25 miles from the Ford factory in Hegeswisch, IL, so Ford purchased 1,440 acres of farm land in nearby Lansing, IL (south of Chicago) and in nearby Munster, IN. He erected a hangar (also designed by Kahn) and in January 1927 he had established his own operational airfield. A small Verville biplane was purchased to run the US Mail from Lansing, IL to the government airfield at Maywood. The Lansing airport, sold in 1937, is still in use today and the hangar was placed on the National Register of Historical Places May 9, 1985. Always looking to maximize assets and minimize expenses, Ford leased the outlying acres back to the farmers for a share of their produce. In December 1930 the airport manager, complaining the market for corn was only 60 cents a bushel, requested approval to hold 2,000

Not all flights went right all the time. 2AT-6, *Maiden Dearborn V* after a "rough" landing. Note open hatch over pilot's compartment and mooring mast in background. (Hudek FMC 189.3296)

Model T truck, made of Monel metal, was used to transport mail and freight between Ford plants and the airports. Monel metal, a copper and nickel alloy, resists corrosion allowing the polished metal to retain its luster. (Henry Ford Museum FMC 833.43618)

bushels until after the first of the year for a better price. Ford employees have always been versatile!

Ford's service was the first regularly scheduled airline in the US dedicated to one company. It was not intended, nor utilized, as a passenger carrier (with the exception of a few company personnel being carried only with management approval). It was also the first airline to run by the clock, and when a plane took off the time was duly noted as the aircraft roared over nearby Ford Headquarters. For the Air Transport Service, Ford purchased Stout's second 2AT which was the first plane built at the new factory provided by Ford. Starting with flights every other day, it increased to daily service when the next Stout

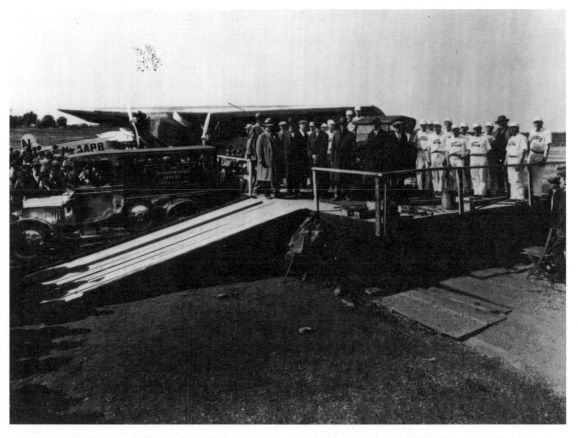

4AT-1 at Buffalo, NY. 16 Ford employees have just finished assembling a Model T car in 28 minutes from parts brought in on the Ford plane. (Henry Ford Museum FMC 189.3747)

plane became available on April 27th. As more planes were built, service was extended from Dearborn-to-Cleveland on July 1, 1925 and Dearborn-to-Buffalo on March 28, 1927. To dramatize the convenience, versatility and practicality of air freight and help add drama to the dedication of the new Cleveland Municipal Airport, Ford shipped all the parts for a Model T car on the first Cleveland flight and had 17 employees from the local Ford assembly plant unload and assemble the car at the airport in one hour and three minutes after the plane landed. A Cleveland-to-Buffalo run was subsequently added using local existing hangar facilities, but lasted only ten months. Here again, the transport of parts for a Model T car and its assembly on arrival in Buffalo created desired publicity for Ford. To further help publicize Ford's aviation interests, specially built, highly polished Monel metal trucks marked *Air Transportation Service of Ford Motor Company* provided service between the factories and airports in Dearborn, Cleveland and Chicago. The Ford

Air Transport Service continued until August 1932, by which time Ford had demonstrated the economic feasibility and safety of air transportation and felt there were sufficient other airlines available to service his needs. The Ford Air Transport Service planes had traveled almost two million miles, carrying nearly thirteen million pounds of freight and mail, with only two fatal accidents. They had completed 93% of their 10,149 scheduled flights, with only 58 cancellations due to mechanical problems, 30 of which were with the early single engine 2ATs in the first two years of operations.

All operating and cost information obtained from the operation of Ford's experimental Air Transport Service was freely shared with the aviation industry on a regular basis. In August of 1925 Herbert Hoover, then Secretary of the Department of Commerce (which was responsible for US aviation), wrote Henry Ford thanking him for providing operating costs for the Chicago-Detroit-Cleveland air service. Based on their own experience, Ford's airplane catalogs of 1927 and 1928 devoted a great deal of space to suggestions on the organization and financing of an airline along with general information about the requirements of the typical landing field. In a January 1928 ad they wrote **"Write direct to us for any information you may desire."**

United States Air Mail Contract

On September 21, 1925, when the Postmaster General advertised for bids under the recently enacted Kelly Air Mail Act (providing for private contractors to carry the air mail), Ford Motor Company was already operating a daily scheduled air service and was fully committed to the development of commercial aviation. However, Ford had also been working quietly behind the scenes to assure that he was awarded the Contract Air Mail (CAM) 7 contract (Detroit-to-Chicago). His people had been visiting postal officials since as early as July to assure that they (the Post Office) **"have their advertisement in line with what we can do."** Because of their concern for the success of the private air mail scheme, postal officials were extremely wary of inexperienced and financially weak groups winning bids, and they were certainly delighted that Ford was interested and would probably have done almost anything to assure the acceptance of his proposal.

On January 10th, 1926 Postmaster Charles Kellogg of Detroit announced that Ford planes would begin carrying the mail on CAM 6 (Detroit-to-Cleveland) and CAM 7 (Detroit-to-Chicago), February 1, 1926. On January 12th Ford was advised these flights would be delayed until February 15, 1926 in order to allow Washington based postal officials to participate in the inaugural ceremonies. An interesting footnote is the fact that although Ford Airport was located in Dearborn, Dearborn was not in the Detroit Postal District and, therefore, not part of the Contract Air Mail route. The local Postmaster was

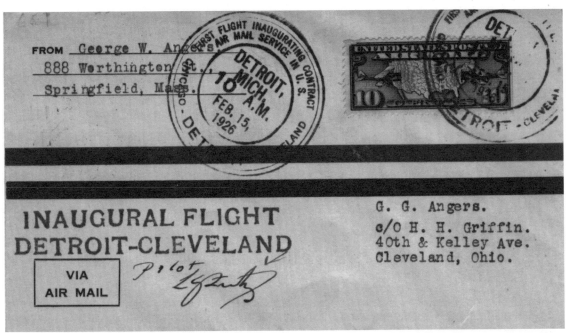

First Ford Flight postal cover for (Contract Air Mail route) CAM 6, Detroit-to-Cleveland, signed by pilot Lawrence Fritz. Carries the DETROIT commemorative postmark. These types of covers made up most of the mail on the first flight. (O'Callaghan)

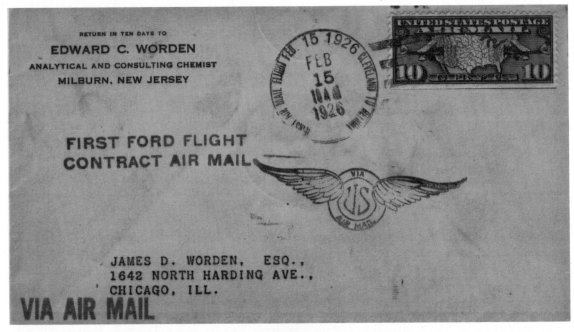

Return flight CAM 6, Cleveland-to-Detroit. The DETROIT commemorative postmark was applied to the back of the envelope on mail carried on the return flight. (O'Callaghan)

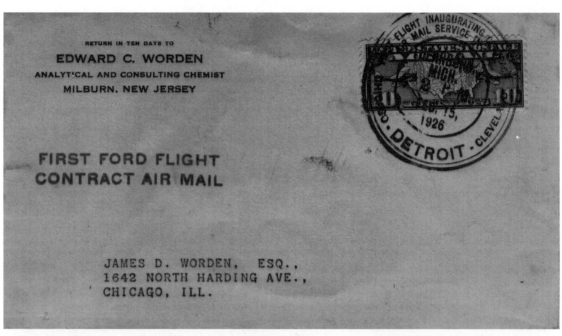

First flight cover for CAM 7, Detroit-to-Chicago, with the scarcer DEARBORN postmark. Both DETROIT and DEARBORN covers were flown on the same flight. (O'Callaghan)

Return flight, Chicago-to-Detroit on CAM 7. The large DETROIT postmark was also applied to the back of mail on this return flight. This envelope also carries cancellation for Feb 13, 1925, which was the first day of issue for the new airmail stamp issued to commemorate the new, private Contract Air Mail routes. (O'Callaghan)

Ford Pilot Lawrence Fritz in typical flight gear. Fritz would fly the first Contract Air Mail flight, Dearborn-to-Cleveland, on February 15, 1926. Fritz became an Air Force Major General in World War II and an American Airlines Vice President after the war. (Hudek FMC 189.4082)

United States Air Mail Flyer's Medal of Honor was authorized Feb 14, 1931 to be awarded for acts of heroism performed between May 15, 1918 and August 12, 1970. First recipient was Mal Freeburg, flying a Ford Tri-Motor for Northwest Airways in 1932. A total of ten medals were awarded, the last in 1948 for an act performed in 1938. (US Post Office Department)

great future for commercial airmail with 249 pounds carried on both routes at $1.08 a pound. Unfortunately, most was stamp collectors mail and over the next twenty nine months their average flight would carry just over 10 pounds of mail and generate only $11 in revenues. Interestingly, Ford and the Post Office disagreed on how much weight was carried during February 1926 and they exchanged lengthy letters over a two ounce (13 cents) difference on CAM 6 and a four pound ($4.32) difference on CAM 7. And, while early in 1925 they had offered to fly the Air Mail without compensation to help the Post Office develop data to base its rates and schedules, they now were arguing that their proposal to carry the mail should have been at the rate of 67.5% of total revenue instead of 6.75¢ an ounce quoted in their bid. They lost!

The first Ford air fatality and the first fatality under the new Air Mail service occurred on May 18, 1926 at Argo, IL (Chicago) when Ford pilot Ross Kirkpatrick crashed in the *Maiden Dearborn I* while attempting to land in **"poor visibility caused by fog, smoke, haze and rain."** This was the only fatal accident in a

not able to resolve this ridiculous situation until shortly before February 15th, with the result that few First Flight envelopes bear the distinctive Dearborn Post Office cancellation. When February 15th was over, it promised a

Ford operated 2AT, but it seemed to have crystallized Ford's thinking concerning his aviation policy as related by Charles Lindbergh at a later date:

Make monoplanes because they were simpler.
Make them out of metal because metal was the thing of the future.
Make them with more than one engine because they weren't going to have any more forced landings.

Lindbergh commented that Henry Ford had laid down three of the fundamentals that had formed the base of successful air transport development and described this as **"an instance when his genius came out with exceptional clarity."**

In March of 1927 the Post Office inquired if Ford was interested in the Detroit-to-Buffalo mail contract. Ford replied in the affirmative, but only with the guarantee of 150 pounds of mail daily. The Post Office never pursued the discussion.

On July 19, 1928 the airmail contracts CAM 6 and 7 were terminated by Ford. No reasons for this decision have been found, but Ford had pioneered another phase of aviation carrying 32,031 pounds of mail. It is probable that Ford was influenced by the fact that the publicity value of being first with the mail was gone and the meager mail revenues came nowhere near covering the addi-

tional costs of providing the administrative and security services required by the Post Office contract.

An interesting sidelight to Ford and US Air Mail Service is the fact that three of the first eight Air Mail Flyers Medal of Honor recipients were flying Ford Tri-Motor planes when they performed their heroic deeds:

April 12, 1932	Mal Freeburg (1st) Northwest Airways
February 10, 1933	Eddie Bellande TWA
April 21, 1935	James Carmichael Central Airlines

Pilot Training

Ford's Air Transport Service also served as a vehicle for training pilots for the new owners of the Tri-Motor planes and many of these Ford trained pilots went on to become leaders in the early aviation industry. In June 1925, shortly after the Ford Air Transport Service was started, Mayo wrote to William Cowling, a senior Ford executive that:

"It is our intention in breaking in new pilots to hire them at the Stout Plant and put them through a course of work on the plane and later transfer them to the Air Port."

Tri-Motor pilots were either men nominated by the buyer for training by Ford or a few Ford pilots kept on the payroll to be available to a new purchaser. Ford was concerned about his (and his airplane's) reputation and wanted qualified pilots flying Ford planes. In February 1929 he advertised:

"Purchasers of planes are welcome to send their own men to the school for this special training, if they meet the requirements. But we must ask them to consider our decision of their fitness final.

So important do we regard this provision, that we reserve the right to decline to deliver a Ford plane unless the pilot who will fly it meets with the approval of the officials of our training school."

A 1931 letter to a potential pilot spelled out Ford's requirements. They included 700 hours prior flying time and stated that most successful applicants were ex-Army pilots who had trained on all types of planes. If a preflight checkout with the chief Ford pilot was satisfactory, they proceeded to spend about 30 hours flying for Ford's Air Transport Service, combined with working about a month in various departments of the airplane manufacturing plant to become familiar with the construction of the plane.

Salary and wage information is skimpy, but the pay records, complete with observations, of three of the first pilots employed by Ford were found in the Ford Motor Company Industrial Archives.

Comments on Pay Record

Edward Hamilton		From Stout Metal Airplane Company
Jun 1, 1925	$500	
Aug 1, 1927	550	Operations Superintendent
May 31, 1928	quit	Purchased Ford plane. First class man. Top executive.

LeRoy Sherman Manning		Former Army pilot
Jun 1, 1925	$400	
Jul 1, 1928	450	
Dec 1, 1928	500	In charge of operation & all test work
Dec 1, 1929	580	
Jul 1, 1930	625	
Sep 19, 1931	killed	Pay salary until Dec 31, 1931 (Flight mechanic too.)

Lawrence Fritz		From Aerial Surveys of Cleveland
Aug 1, 1925	$250	Assistant pilot
Oct 1, 1925	300	Full fledged pilot
Apr 1, 1926	325	
Oct 1, 1926	350	
Apr 1, 1927	375	
Jul 30, 1927	quit	Flew plane to Maddux Airlines in California and joined them. Would rehire.

By way of comparison, Carl Wenzel, one of the first employees transferred to the Airplane Division and a flight-test mechanic, was being paid $265 a month at the time of his death in the crash of a Ford plane in November 1930. In eight years of manufacturing airplanes and operating the Air Transport Service, Ford Motor Company had only five fatal accidents:

Air Transport Service: May 18, 1925, Ross Kirkpatrick in a 2AT

May 12, 1928, William Munn & Earl Parker in a 4AT

Airplane Division: Feb 25, 1928, Harry Brooks in a Flivver

Nov. 24, 1930, Myron Zeller & Carl Wenzel in a 5AT

Sept. 19, 1931, LeRoy Manning & L. H. Garriott in the XB906

4

THE STOUT METAL AIRPLANE COMPANY

The Purchase

Henry Ford decided that if Stout's airplane company was going to amount to anything it needed a large amount of capital and that he was the one to provide it. By June 1925 Mayo was requesting a list from the Rouge Employment Office of those employees who were pilots or had experience with airplane engines. On August 1, 1925 it was announced that Ford Motor Company had purchased all assets and stock of the Stout Metal Airplane Company as of July 31, 1925. Henry Ford, still smarting from several minority stockholders holding up his purchase of the D T & I Railroad in 1920 and the Dodge Brothers minority stockholders suit in 1917, had told Stout that he would buy the company only if he got 100% of the stock. This was accomplished by paying each of the stockholders $2 for each $1 invested with Bill Stout and his working associates getting slightly more. The Stout Metal Airplane Company became a division of the Ford Motor Company for $1,300,000: $200,000 for assets, inventory and three planes in process and the balance for developmental costs.

Stout had all the investors' money funneled through him, allowing him, he claimed, to persuade all but three of the original investors to reinvest their money in his new Stout Air Service Company, formed to start the first scheduled passenger airline in the United States between Dearborn and Grand Rapids, MI. Stanley Knauss, his General Manager and records of the Stout Air Service indicate only 63 of his original investors participated in his new venture. George Goin was placed in charge of aircraft manufacturing with Alex Runkis as his assistant. Although Stout remained on Ford's payroll, he had previously planned to start an airline and persuaded Henry Ford to allow him to proceed at this time as a means of getting the Stout stockholders to sell out to Ford. They had invested in Detroit aviation and several were reluctant to see Henry Ford grab Stout's company. Stout claimed, **"I had twice the job to un-sell the stock as I ever did to sell it."** It was Stout's airline, The Stout Air Service, incidentally, not Ford's Air Transport Service, that started the practice of uniforms for pilots and flight stewards. Early Ford Air Transport Service pilots flew open cockpit planes, wore heavy flight overalls and never carried paying passengers, so they had no need for uniforms or flight attendants. Because of the closeness of the Ford/Stout aviation connection, many people have assumed that the Ford Air Transport Service and the Stout Air Service lines were one and the same.

The Planes

A brief summary of "who built what" will probably make the following discussion more understandable:

William Stout, as owner of the Stout Metal Airplane Company, designed and built the following planes:

AS-1	Air Sedan	All Metal 4 passenger
AP-1	Air Pullman	All Metal 8 persons (named *Maiden Detroit* and later referred to as 2AT-1)
2AT-2 thru 5	Air Transport	All Metal 8 persons (sold to Ford and named *Maiden Dearborn I, II, III & IV*)

William Stout as the manager of the Stout Metal Airplane Company, Division of Ford Motor Company, designed and built the following planes:

2AT-6 thru 11	Air Transport	All Metal 8 persons
3AT	Air Transport	All Metal three engine plane

Ford engineers of the Stout Metal Airplane Company, Division of Ford Motor Company, designed and built the following planes:

4AT	Air Transport	All Metal three engine, 12 passenger
5AT	Air Transport	All Metal three engine, 14 passenger

Air Transport, 2AT

The Air Transport, or 2AT, was designed to carry six people or 1,500 pounds of freight, plus a pilot and copilot and was built with an eye towards capturing some of the Post Office's air mail business, which at the time was using war surplus DeHavilands with only a 500 pound capacity. They had an uphill fight with the air mail pilots however, as they were comfortable with their DeHavilands due to their surplus power and maneuverability and the pilots were reluctant to change to the larger, less agile 2AT which used the same 400hp Liberty engine. In addition, the cockpit on the 2AT was located in front of the wing for better visibility and to develop passenger confidence. However, the airmail pilots felt that just put them closer to the danger in case of a crash. Also, the other newly formed air services were not interested in carrying passengers but only the air mail for the government subsidy and so viewed the size and price of the 2AT as excessive to their needs.

The first 2AT was designed for a pilot and copilot, but when sold to the Post Office was

Stout's second all metal plane and first 2AT. It was called an Air Pullman and named the *Maiden Detroit*, i.e. made in Detroit. Air Mail pilots are wearing typical flying gear. Full wind screen was only used on this first 2AT. (Hudek FMC 1008.AP2097)

LeRoy Manning, Ford pilot, by *Maiden Dearborn II*, in a rare photograph showing the round Stout Metal Airplane medallion. This medallion was used briefly prior to Ford's purchase of Stout's company. (Hudek)

2AT-2 *Maiden Dearborn* being towed into Ford hangar. Renamed *Maiden Dearborn I* when Ford added second plane to his fleet. (Hudek FMC 833.43622)

changed to a single seat as only one pilot was used and visibility was not as good with a double seat. This first plane was also built with a full celluloid windshield and quick opening side windows. Future 2ATs would be built as both single and dual seat planes depending on whether they would be used forced or crash landings in these 2ATs and the Tri-Motors, several of which were fatal, there is no record of a Ford pilot parachuting from his plane. The first five 2ATs used by Ford for freight operations were entered by the pilot climbing up the side of the plane to the cockpit using toe holes built into the side

Miss St Petersburg departing Ford Airport in Dec 1925. Four of these 2ATs were sold to Florida Airways and were the last 2ATs built. (Hudek FMC 189.3195)

for freight or passenger service and only had small frontal windscreens. In addition there was a partial cover over the cockpit area, hinged at the rear, for ease of access and quick departure in case of an emergency. Interestingly, while Ford pilots had a number of of the fuselage. As the planes used by Wanamaker and Florida Airways were for passenger service, the pilots entered the cockpit of these planes through the passenger cabin. The second 2AT, which was the first built at the new Stout factory at Ford Airport, was

First Tri-Motor 3AT was ugly from either angle and an aerodynamic disaster. Note open cockpit on top of plane. Destroyed in a mysterious fire at the Stout airplane factory in January 1926. (Hudek FMC 189.3172 top, and FMC 189.3177 bottom)

Stout Metal Airplane factory after the January 17, 1926 fire. Stout's name would not appear on future Ford buildings. (Henry Ford Museum FMC 833.45237)

2AT-2, *Maiden Dearborn*, was first plane produced in Stout's new factory built by Ford. (Hudek)

christened *Maiden Dearborn*, later renamed *Maiden Dearborn I* when the second ship was christened *Maiden Dearborn II*. Ford purchased this first ship for his newly created Air Transport Service for $22,500 ($20,000 for the plane plus $2,500 for the engine). After Ford decided to start his own air service he arranged to purchase from the government twenty surplus Liberty engines, he had originally produced during the war, for $2,000 each and then purchased the next 2ATs from Stout for $20,000 each. Stout's cost on these planes was estimated at

$15,000. The seventh 2AT, sold to the John Wanamaker & Company in October 1925, was the first commercial sale of a Ford plane. Wanamaker had sold the first Ford car in the New York District and wanted to be the one to sell the first Ford plane. It was publicly displayed for sale in Wanamaker's New York store and then repurchased in January 1926 by the Stout Air Service for their Detroit-to-Grand Rapids route. The last four planes were sold on December 28, 1925 to a new company, Florida Airways, and stayed sold a little longer. Florida Airways, whose co-founders included World War I ace Eddie Ricken-backer, and had William Mayo on the Board of Directors, ceased operations in December 1926 with one 2AT destroyed in a hurricane, two purchased by Stout Air Service and one by Ford Air Transport Service. All 2ATs were grounded July 20, 1928 as it was not feasible to meet the new Department of Commerce aircraft licensing requirements - specifically: structural weakness in the wings. This in spite of the fact one had flown over 132,000 miles and collectively they had just one weather related fatality.

The earliest documented use of the nickname *Tin Goose* was in connection with this single engine Ford plane, not the famous Tri-Motor that followed. A December 30, 1925 head-line in a Monroe, MI newspaper read, **"One of Henry's Tin Geese is storm victim"** referring to one of the four planes delivered to Florida Airways. The following day another article was headed **"3 Tin Geese in Wreck, Nashville."**

The Tri-Motor Planes

Ford was convinced by now that the future of commercial aviation lay in larger multi-engine ships for economy of size and safety and as soon as new lightweight, high perfor-mance engines became available, had Stout working on a three engine plane. By Novem-ber 1925, Stout had modified the structure of one of the single engine 2ATs by widen-ing the center wing section by ten feet, strengthening the fuselage and landing gear and placing two of the new 200hp Wright J-4 radial air cooled engines in the wings and one in the nose. The open cockpit was lo-cated on top of, and just in front of, the wing. It was designated 3AT and it was ugly and an aerodynamic disaster. Maj. Schroeder con-ducted the first test flight November 24, 1925 and refused to take the plane up for further tests. It is reported that Schroeder had in fact stated during construction that placing the engines in the wings was not practical, cit-ing the poor experience of German compa-nies. Contemporary Ford Motor Company motion picture film shows an early model of the 3AT with the outboard engines located **on top of the wings!** Henry Ford, who had high hopes for this plane, had another Ford pilot, Larry Fritz, test the plane with the same results. Ford was furious as he had a failure on his hands and on January 17, 1926 the airplane factory, with the 3AT inside, myste-riously burned to the ground. Eight days later on January 25th, Stout had a proposal ready to build another three engine plane almost identical to the hated 3AT. It was shortly af-ter this that Henry Ford is quoted as saying, **"that for the first time in my life I have bought a lemon, and I don't want the world to know about it,"** and Bill Stout was sent off on an extended public relations tour. There was never an official explanation of the fire but many people connected with the airplane operations at the time felt certain that Henry Ford had the plant burned down to eliminate the plane and his failure. A memo

First Ford 4AT Tri-Motor built June 1926. Note open cockpit and half moon windows similar to the earlier 2AT. Early 4ATs were later rebuilt to more modern standards. (Hudek FMC 189.3431)

Ford Tri-Motor 5AT-112, March 1932, one of the last planes built. Note the rounded tail. Probably an attempt to modernize the Tri-Motor. This and the XB906 were the only planes built with this tail. (Hudek FMC 0.3426)

dated January 19, 1926 directed that the loss be stated to the Dearborn Fire Department as $71,515.48 for the building and $404,892.76 for the contents. Total insurance coverage was listed as $39,000. Various reports state the losses included the 3AT Tri-Motor, the Post Office's 2AT (formerly the *Maiden Detroit*), two or three other 2AT's under construction, a new $10,000 Packard 500hp engine, and between 13 and 54 new Wright J-4 engines valued at $4,500 each. The larger number of these Wright engines is unlikely as they were new and scarce.

On April 13, 1926 Ford announced that **"Planes manufactured from now on will be of the multi-motored type with three air-cooled engines."** This announcement must be considered in the context of the times to appreciate its full impact. In 1926 only six of 28 American commercial plane manufacturers were listed as building a multi-engine aircraft. In reality the only one available for purchase was Fokker's F.VIIa-3m made of a fabric covered wooden frame. Fokker had successfully added two engines to his single engine F.VIIa to take advantage of the expo-

5AT-15 used by Stout Air Lines. First airline to use uniformed personnel and flight attendants. (Hudek FMC 189.6230)

Ford Tri-Motors were equipped with wheels, skis and pontoons. This plane, 5AT-74 (with wheels) is currently owned and operated by Scenic Airlines in Las Vegas, NV. (William Larkins)

sure afforded by the first Ford National Air Tour held in September 1925. Ford's decision was quite far sighted given the prevailing concepts and opinions.

The new three engine airplane (4AT) designed by Ford engineers was developed and test flown by Maj. Schroeder on the morning of June 11, 1926 (only five months after the fire). With the fiasco of the 3AT fresh in mind, only Henry and Edsel Ford, and a few Ford executives, witnessed this first flight. In the afternoon the plane was demonstrated before a large crowd. In a July press release Ford touted one of Stout's ideas:

"The outstanding feature of the plane, and one which has a big safety element, is the extreme vision afforded the pilot and mechanic, who sit in front of the cabin in advance of the wing, which allows each of them to see in every direction on both sides of the plane. It is said to be the first time the vision problem has really been solved in a big plane - the most serious problem of all in the

construction of large airplanes."

Stout also felt the pilot would be a little more alert if he was going to be the first one injured!

This first plane, while a great success, would undergo many refinements in the next several years resulting in a plane, while looking very much like the 4AT1, was really quite different. The first planes had an open cockpit, thanks to Maj. Schroeder's insistence, a tail skid and no brakes. An open cockpit was considered essential by most pilots of the era so that they could feel the wind on their face, hear the sound of the wind in the guy wires and get out quickly with a parachute. All of these early planes were later rebuilt with closed cockpits, brakes and tail wheels. They were powered by three Wright J-4 engines of 200hp each and accommodated 12 passengers. Later versions carried engines generating a total of over 1,200hp vs the 600hp in the 4AT-A series. In July 1928 the 5AT was introduced, a faster model with more powerful engines, a larger wing span and 14 passenger capacity. It proved to be the most successful all metal, multi-engine passenger plane in the United States, being used by virtually all airlines of the period. The other models, 6AT, 7AT, 8AT, 9AT, 11AT and 13AT were modified 4AT and 5AT airframes with different engine combinations.

In July 1929, T. A. T. (Transcontinental Air Transport) and the Pennsylvania and Santa Fe Railroads combined to offer **"Coast to Coast, Two days by plane - Two nights by train."** As an indication of the Ford Tri-Motor's reputation at the time, the technical committee of T. A.T., which included Charles Lindbergh and Major Thomas Lamphier, selected and ordered 11 Ford Tri-Motors, because as their literature stated:

"Over a period of years, operating through the four seasons and daily schedule service, Ford planes have compiled a record of millions of miles of safe, comfortable, 'on time' flight that may well be compared with the records of our greatest railroads."

Other major customers for new Ford Tri-Motor airplanes were:

Army, Navy & Marines	22
Maddux Air Line	16
National Air Transport	11
Southwest Air Fast Express	10
Pan American	9
Stout Air Service	8

In addition, multiple plane orders were received from Robertson Aircraft Corp., Curtis Flying Service, Northwest Airways, Cia Mexicana de Aviacion, Colonial Air Transport, Pacific Air Transport and others.

The sales department consisted mainly of William Mayo, whose many aviation connections (and the massive Ford aviation advertising program) generated most leads. Later on he was assisted by several outside salesmen.

In 1926, observing how the tail skids on planes were tearing up the airport sod, Ford engineers C. J. Smith and Harold Hicks developed and patented the first airplane tailwheel. This, and the use of concrete runways, led to brakes on planes which previously were slowed by the friction of the tailskid. Ford Tri-Motor 4AT11, built in October of 1927, was the first Ford plane equipped with a tail wheel. Interestingly, most Ford pilots refused to test the first plane, fearing they would lose control in landing. By 1930 Ford held (or had applied for) 35 aviation related patents, including brakes, stabilizers, shock absorbers, wing mail bins, wing lights, radio beacons and airplane superchargers. Ford

4AT-1 at Selfridge airfield, Mt. Clemens, MI. The number of people using the wing for a grandstand gives an idea of the strength of the 34 inch thick wings. (Henry Ford Museum FMC 189.3725)

levied no fee on others for use of his patents stating, **"We take patents on our own developments or discoveries only to prevent others from freezing us out when they may chance to make the same discovery."**

The last Tri-Motor, 5AT116, was delivered to Pan American Airways in June 1933. Selling prices ranged from $42,000 for the early 4ATs to $60,000 for a 5AT D model in 1932, with Ford's and the engine manufacturer's warranty covering parts for 90 days.

Much has been written about how many Model T automobile parts were used in the Ford planes, especially the use of the Model T steering wheel. But Bob Baron, an inspector for the Airplane Division from 1925 to 1937, states that there were only five common parts. The major item was the **Johnson Bar** brake lever from the Lincoln. In addition, there were three twist cap reflector lights on the instrument panel, four ball caps used on the stabilizer brace strut, the door handle and lock assembly and, finally, individual ashtrays which were available on the open market.

In June 1925 Ford Accounting Instructions had directed that Ford planes be depreciated 20% a year and that engines be written off in 500 hours. By 1930, Ford's sale brochure proclaimed, **"No Ford Plane Has Ever Worn Out,"** and indeed, a Ford survey in 1945 found 90 Tri-Motors were still flying, most in South and Central America. Today, 61 years later, five planes are still in flying condition, three are fully restored in museums and three or more are actively under restoration.

The all metal, three engine Ford Tri-Motor airplane, backed by the Ford name, revolutionized the public's conception of safety in air travel. Most of today's airlines started with Ford 4ATs and the larger 5ATs and they dominated the industry until Ford relinquished the business to the Boeing 247s and Douglas DC 2s and 3s in the mid 1930's.

5

THE NEW FACTORY AND BUILDINGS

Exterior of new hangar. All doors, on both sides, rolled back into the ends of the building. It was the most modern and probably the largest hangar ever built at that time. (Henry Ford Museum FMC 189.4464)

The Hangar

After the airplane factory was destroyed in January 1926, development of the new 4AT was moved to a portion of the Engineering Laboratory building while a new factory, designed by Albert Kahn, was being built. A huge new hangar capable of housing at least 15 planes, that was to be larger and entirely different from any currently existing, was underway by March of 1926 to handle the anticipated requirements generated by the new larger airplane factory. It was 123' x 300' of buff brick, with 32 steel and glass doors

Aerial view of Ford Airport showing old and new hangars and airplane factory about 1927. Note foreground letters R and D of the FORD name along the runway. (Hudek)

extending the full 300 feet on both sides and with all doors being fully retractable into the ends of the building. The roof was built on a cantilever plan extending on each side from a row of steel towers in the center of the building. At the same time a dynamometer room was being added to the old hangar building. This hangar was to be relegated to maintenance and repair for airplanes operating in the Ford Air Transport service. By 1929 the Government had a weather bureau office located in it and twice daily took balloon readings from the hangar roof.

The Factory

By November 1926 the new factory, 500' x 124' of Bedford limestone and fireclay brick, also designed by Kahn, was completed to produce the new Tri-Motor airplane. The new factory was 60,000 square feet, three times the size of the destroyed plant, with a steel and glass roof extending the full 124 foot width from wall to wall (without intervening supports). This new building, standing partially on the site of the former Stout factory, <u>did</u> <u>not</u> <u>bear</u> <u>the</u> <u>Stout</u> <u>name</u>!

Plans called for production of one plane every two weeks produced by the **"Ford system of progressive production, now to be applied to airplane manufacturing for the first time."** By March of 1929 plans were being made for producing one plane every two days! In June 1929, it was announced the airplane factory would be increased to 640' x 258' (165,120 square feet), allowing for production of one plane a day, with 12 planes on the trim line and consolidation of parts making operations from other locations. The *Ford News* for August 1, 1929 announced that, **"Production of Ford Tri-Motor all-metal monoplanes broke all existing records during the month of June.**

Interior of new hangar with space for about fifteen aircraft. The roof extended from a row of steel towers in the center of the building providing for an unobstructed area. (Henry Ford Museum FMC 189.4534)

First section of new airplane factory with new hangar on right. (Hudek, segment of FMC 189.6603)

A total of twenty five were trimmed and eighteen were test flown.'' Ironically, this proved to be the high water mark for Ford airplane production as from September 1929 on, no more than five planes a month would be built.

Available employment data is sketchy. While some people have claimed as many as 1,500 employees and the *New York Times* reported 1,200 in January 1929 (which was about the peak time for production), existing records show far fewer. Company records indicate 108 employees in April 1926, 150 in November 1926, 150 in August 1930, 500 in December 1930 and 263 by April 1932. Airplane production workers earned an average of 81¢ an hour in 1926.

Radio Beacon and Telephone

To facilitate all weather flying, the dangers

54

and cancellations caused by rain, fog and darkness had to be overcome. To this end Ford engineers, proceeding on earlier developmental work by the Bureau of Standards and the US Air Service, perfected the radio beacon for use in commercial aviation application. The first successful radio guided flight between airfields (while both were signaling) took place in a snow storm on February 10, 1926. A Ford Tri-Motor, flown by Ford pilot Harry Brooks, made a round trip flight between Ford Airport, Dearborn, MI and McCook Field, Dayton, OH, the pilot being guided the entire way by radio bea-

Airplane factory employee Anthony Saley working on control cable. Note employee badge on breast pocket. (Robert Baron)

Rare Ford Airplane Factory badge. Peak employment estimates during 1929 range from a low of 500 men to a high of 1500 (Actual size is 1 1/4 x 1 1/2 inches). (O'Callaghan)

Center wing section being lowered into place on 5AT model. (Hudek FMC 189.6277)

Ford airplane production line with 5AT-1 being completed. X designation reflects use of experimental Pratt & Whitney Wasp engines. (Hudek)

con. The Ford radio beacon was placed in service October 26, 1926 and carried the call letters W F O. Ford received a patent on this system and in the future all Ford planes carried radios.

Due to the increase in the use of radios on aircraft and the increased volume of air traffic, a radio telephone ground transmitting station that Ford had been experimenting with since 1927 was inaugurated June 16, 1930 with call letters W Q D W.

Airport Terminal

To accommodate the new Stout Air Service passenger line, an airport terminal building, again designed by Kahn, was built and opened in November 1927. Looking much like a small train station of the period, it was

Passenger terminal built to service the Stout Air Service passenger line and the Ford Air Transport Service. Bus service was available to downtown Detroit. Another first for Henry Ford. (Henry Ford Museum FMC 189.5163)

Interior of passenger terminal building with complete passenger lounge. Offices for Stout Air Service and Ford Air Transport Service were located on second floor. (Hudek FMC 189.5159)

a two story affair (52' x 52' first floor and 28' x 28' second floor) constructed of white brick, stone and Spanish tile similar to the new airplane factory. It had offices on the second floor for both the Ford Air Transport Service and the Stout Air Service operations and a well equipped passenger lounge and ticket office on the first floor. In addition, the first airport limousine service was started by Detroit Streets and Railways to service downtown Detroit and the first airline ticket office in the US was set up in the Book Cadil-

lac Hotel in Detroit. A glassed-in control room was added to the top of the building in 1945.

Dearborn Inn

To service the air traveler, the 100 room Dearborn Inn, designed by Albert Kahn in the Early American Period style, was opened across the street from the terminal building on July 1, 1931, one of the first US hotels specifically built to service airport traffic. R. T. Walker, Mayo's secretary, states that Edsel Ford, feeling that airlines and everything pertaining to aeronautics was modern, felt the terminal and inn should also be modern. Edsel won his argument with the terminal but Henry Ford insisted on Early American for the inn. The Statler Hotel organization was chosen to run the inn, but Henry Ford forbid alcoholic beverages and banned smoking, both of which Statler management permit-

ted. Rather than create an enemy of Henry Ford they declined the management contract. Management of the inn was then turned over to the Treadway Corporation who ran a chain of Early American inns in the east and operated Ford's Wayside Inn in Sudbury, MA. A contemporary brochure lists: **"Single room with tub and shower - $3.50."**

The Dearborn Inn was opened July 1, 1931 to service airport customers. It was one of first inns in the world built to handle the anticipated flow of air travelers. (Hudek FMC 833.56398.1)

6

ADVERTISING AND PROMOTION

Advertising

The Stout Metal Airplane Company became an operating Division of Ford Motor Company on August 1, 1925 and the Stout name was featured in ads in the form of an oval medallion with a winged Ford in the center surrounded by the words The Stout Metal Airplane Company. The first use of this 12" x 18" medallion on an aircraft was on the 2AT plane sold by Ford Motor Company to the John Wanamaker Company in October 1925. As Ford used all previous planes in his own Air Transport Service and they were all marked with large Ford script on both sides of the fuselage and carried large block **FORD** letters under the wings, no nameplate was previously needed. The medallion was placed on all aircraft built or operated by Ford through 4AT51 and 5AT5, both of which were built in early November 1928. The medallion was located near the nose on the early production planes and beside the passenger door on later planes, obviously to create greater passenger awareness. The medal-

First version of Ford's identification plaque. Painted on 2AT-7 and replaced when the logo was rendered in metal. (Hudek, segement of FMC 189.3085)

lion was last used in Ford advertising in December 1927. However, The Stout Metal Airplane Company name was used in advertisements until December 1929. R. T. Walker claimed the switch from Stout's name was prompted by Ford's desire to profit from any publicity and the feeling that the identification of the Ford name with aviation, via the Ford Tri-Motor, would prove more beneficial to the aviation industry than the continued use of the Stout name.

The value of the Ford name in establishing the safety and reliability of commercial aviation (and as something other than what barnstormers did on weekends) should not be underestimated. Henry Ford had made it possible for the average man to own a car and was literally worshiped by millions of people around the world. The prevailing attitude was that if Henry Ford was involved in it, it must be OK.

Stout Metal Airplane Company, Division of Ford Motor Co., medallion (12 inches by 18 inches) on Richard Byrd's Antarctic plane 4AT-15. The medallion was first used on the Wanamaker 2AT plane in October 1925 and was last used on Tri-Motor planes built in November 1928. (Proctor)

Ford's first ad promoting aviation and the new all metal Tri-motor was a centerfold in *Aviation* magazine on August 15, 1927 declaring,

13AT and single engine 8AT at Detroit Air Show in 1931. 13AT was 5AT-100 modified by replacing normal 420hp Wasps with a 575hp Wright Cyclone and two 300hp Wright J-6 engines. (Hudek)

"The interest and resources of the Ford Motor Company are squarely behind the development of aviation and production of the Ford monoplane." N. W. Ayers & Son of Philadelphia handled Ford's campaign and ran over 100 different ads in aviation and general interest magazines and newspapers promoting aviation and Ford to the general public between 1927 and 1932. *Aero Digest* stated in March 1928, **"His advertising has done more to popularize flying among the reading public than all the stunts that have ever been stunted, at the risk of neck and limb."** And in 1928 Ford was awarded the prestigious Harvard Advertising Award **"for the excellence of their planning and execution in advertising both the Ford Motor Car and the general subject of aviation."** Years later, Ford aviation advertising was included in the book, The 100 Greatest Advertisements, published by Julian Watkins in 1949. The last Ford aviation ad, appropriately enough, offered used planes for sale.

It is noteworthy that most of Ford's early ads promoted the general concept of aviation

Ford Airport at end of the Air Reliability Tour and start of the Detroit News Balloon Trophy Race, July 25, 1931. (Hudek)

rather than the Ford airplane. In July 1929 Ford sent a large, hard cover book entitled <u>Lift Up Your Eyes</u>, to 1,000 top executives in the United States. It contained seventeen of Ford's aviation ads with a cover letter stating:

"It was necessary to induce in the minds of the general public an enthusiastic acceptance of the airplane as a common carrier. We were convinced, therefore, that one of the primary needs of commercial aviation was an advertising campaign to reach the general public."

The National Air Tour

In order to promote aviation among the general public, The Detroit Aviation Society, of which Mayo was President and Edsel Ford a Director, decided to hold an air meet for commercial aircraft at Ford Airport emphasizing reliability and safety, similar to the Glidden

The Edsel B. Ford Trophy awarded during Air Reliability Tours. Trophy was three feet high made of sterling silver on a marble base. Currently on display at Henry Ford Museum. (Hudek FMC 833.46790)

Auto Tours started in 1904 to promote highway travel. The Fords agreed to sponsor the meet and helped organize what was commonly called the Ford Reliability Air Tour (later called the National Air Tours) by offering the use of Ford Airport and donating a magnificent thirty six inch high trophy of sterling silver mounted on a marble base, costing $4,850. It would be permanently awarded to the first manufacturer to win the tour five times, later changed to three. This trophy, called *The Edsel B. Ford Trophy*, took nine months for the silversmiths to create and it is displayed in the Henry Ford Museum. The Tour, starting September 28, 1925, featured seventeen planes from eleven manufacturers flying a prescribed route of 1,775 miles over six days and visiting 13 cities. It was an attempt to demonstrate to the public the safety and reliability of commercial aviation and to stimulate the development of airports by local communities. Ironically, the first fatality at Ford Airport was Ralph Downs, flying trial flights for the Air Tour in a low wing monoplane built by Woodsen in Bryan, OH.

Before the tour could begin, someone had to find out where the planes would land. An airfield in those days could be anything from a farmer's pasture to the County Fairgrounds, but never an airfield as we know it today. A pathfinder trip was undertaken to find and mark these fields and provide local officials with three pages of instructions covering such items as a map of the landing field, field markings, wind socks, aviation gas, mechanics, food, police, judges, referees and last, but not least, publicity. Eleven participants who finished with perfect scores received cash prizes of $350 while a Ford Air Transport Service 2AT, piloted by Edward Hamilton, made the best time for this first tour with an average speed of 101.5 mph. No other plane reached 100 mph! This tour started the ball rolling, for by 1926 many towns and cities had built, were building or were planning to build, real airfields. In addition, Edsel Ford had on December 29, 1925 written to all Ford dealers stating:

"It seems that one of the very great difficulties of cross-country flying is in trying to distinguish over what town or city the pilot is traveling. Therefore, will you not paint on the roof of your garage the name of the city or town in which you are located? Also, an arrow, pointed due north should be painted immediately following the name of the city or town."

The second tour started August 7, 1926 with 16 manufacturers entering 25 planes. This tour covered 2,585 miles in 14 days with stops at 14 cities. The rules were changed this year as two participants earned cash prizes of $2,500 with a Travel Air posting a best speed of 124.1 mph. These tours turned into annual events over the next five years covering mostly midwestern and southern cities. But the longest, and largest, tour in

1928 proceeded from Dearborn, MI to San Antonio, TX to San Diego, CA to Tacoma, WA and back to Dearborn covering 6,304 miles in 29 days. By 1932 the Depression was setting in and Ford wasn't selling many planes. Money was scarce everywhere and many people had already seen many big planes and so the tours just died for lack of interest. Many greats of the aviation world had taken part and Ford planes had won in 1925, 1930 and the last one in 1931, taking permanent possession of *The Edsel B. Ford Trophy.*

Other Promotional Activity

Ford took advantage of most opportunities to promote aviation in general and Ford Airport in particular. In 1925, in connection with the Ford Reliability Air Tour, he promoted and hosted the first Commercial Aeronautical Exposition at Ford Airport and hosted *The Detroit News* sponsored balloon races in both 1925 and 1926. In 1927 and 1928 Ford Airport was host to the famous Gordon Bennett International Balloon Races. Gas facilities for filling the balloons had previously been in-

Edsel Ford, Charles Lindbergh and Henry Ford in airplane factory August 1927. (Henry Ford Museum FMC 189.4588)

Lindbergh's *Spirit of St Louis* in front of hangar at Ford Airport in August 1927. (Ford Motor Co. FMC 189.4559)

stalled for these events. In September 1930, a Ford Tri-Motor, piloted by LeRoy Manning, set a speed record over a 100 kilometer (62.3 miles) closed course for heavy transport planes with a 4,409 pound load of 164.4 miles per hour. In the same month a Ford 5AT model won first place in the multi-engine transport race at the National Air Races in Chicago with an average speed of 144 mph. And finally, in another first, Harold Lloyd's motion picture, *Speedy*, was shown in a Ford Tri-Motor flying over Los Angeles in May 1928. A silent film, naturally, considering the decibel count in a flying Ford!

One more item that's not strictly promotional, but has caused a lot of discussion over the years, was Henry Ford's first ride in an airplane. Charles Lindbergh relates in his book, The War Journals of Charles Lindbergh, that when he visited Ford Airport on August 11, 1927 in his *Spirit of St. Louis*, Henry Ford accepted his invitation for a ride. **"He had to sit crouched up on the arm of my seat in anything but a comfortable position."** Edsel Ford was next to go up with Lindbergh and it was also his first trip in an airplane. Later that same day, Ford took Lindbergh aloft in one of his Tri-Motor airplanes. On

July 12, 1936 Henry Ford was given his third ride in an airplane, a DC 3, sent to Detroit by C. R. Smith, President of American Airlines.

And last of all, did Charles Lindbergh work for Henry Ford? He and six other pilots were hired when the Willow Run Test Flight Department was organized in connection with the building of the B-24 bombers. Ford records indicate he was hired in November 1941 and separated July 28, 1942. His salary was $666.66 a month, Ford badge number S 9. In his Wartime Journals book, Lindbergh indicates he worked with Ford on aviation problems from April 1942 through June 1942 and as an advisor and test pilot for Ford and other aviation companies until March of 1944 when he received permission from the War Department to go the Pacific Theater of operations to evaluate the Corsair airplane under combat conditions.

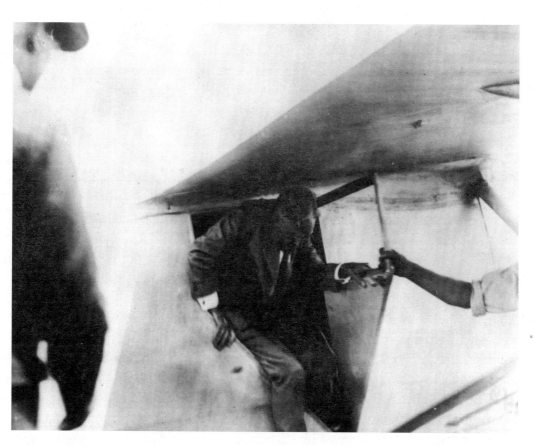

Henry Ford leaving *Spirit of St. Louis* after his first airplane flight. (Henry Ford Museum FMC 833. 49739)

The Literary Digest for October 22, 1927

LOOK TO THE SKIES FOR DAWN

Do you remember the White Ghost?... Or the Red Devil?

Only a few years ago, when automobiles were risky and freakish playthings, those were names to conjure with–phantom machines that dashed at forty miles an hour along graded dirt roads, followed by pillars of dust and fumes of oil, pursued by frantic dogs and the derisive yells of village skeptics. Do you remember the epoch-making Glidden tours across a few hundred miles of New England hills? Do you remember the Vanderbilt Cup Races, with thousands of holiday-makers banked around dangerous curves, *thrilled with the hope of seeing a smash-up?*

Only a few years before that, horses were running wild and cattle stampeding at the hoarse shriek of the locomotive. ...

And prayers were offered regularly for those in peril on the sea.

Remember theses things–*for they happened in our time!*

Today giant liners are ferrying hundreds of thousands of tourists across the oceans. Limited trains glide on roller bearings, safeguarded at every turn of the wheel by automatic controls. And 22,000,000 automobiles have turned the thoughts of everyone in the country outward– outward along smooth highways of asphalt and concrete.

Now look to the skies for dawn!

A new industrial and commercial era is commencing, just as surely as new eras commenced with steamboats, with the railroad, and the automobile. Their dawns were marked with misgivings and catastrophes that befogged the popular vision.... And simi-

larly, the heroic recklessness that the hazards of war made necessary, the dramatic daring of pioneers trying their wings beyond the realms of known safety, the foolish adventures of unskilled fliers in obsolete machines have diverted public attention from what is going on in the solid, safe development of air transportation.

We will awake some early day to realize that a new and tremendous force has entered national life. It does not imply the obsolescence of old-established means of transportation. It means a sudden extension of the capabilities of man–the power to reach hitherto inaccessible spots unerringly and with great swiftness, a means of leaping geographical boundaries in perfect comfort and safety, another triumph over all-consuming Time.

Everyone is familiar with the spectacular achievements in aviation during the past year. Everyone has come to know names such a Le Bourget, Croydon, Tempelhof, Mineola, and the Ford Airport at Detroit–principally because of dramatic events associated with them. But not so many realize that in a recent survey of *one hundred American flying concerns, there were only two fatalities in five million miles of flight.*

The all-metal planes of the Ford Motor Company have already flown on regular schedules, carrying freight, a distance of 700,000 miles... And it is in the well-founded belief that the airplane has brought in a new industrial factor of the first importance, that the Ford Motor company is devoting resources to research, experimentation, and sound production in this new and rapidly expanding field.

FORD MOTOR COMPANY

TIRELESS WINGS

With dust whipping up from the wheels the great limited begins to climb the Sierras, thundering eastward at 45 miles an hour....

The sun sets into the Pacific and rises again out of the Great Plains. An airplane runs across the Field at Los Angeles on cushioned feet and leaps lightly into the air... climbing ...climbing into the clean blue of the California sky ...and away like a homing pigeon for the ridge of the mountains....

An anxious banker travels in the train, racing to meet a vital appointment in New York. A famous satirist travels in the plane, dozing as it wings tirelessly under the stars.

Within 36 hours after leaving the Pacific Coast the satirist is dining in New York. Eighteen hours later he is again halfway across the continent on the return trip! Somewhere above Iowa he looks down at the dim earth below, *and there the great limited train is still thundering eastward carrying the banker who was so anxious to reach New York!*

Business men are looking wide-eyed at the sky. Some stand in a daze watching, speculating. Others, clear-visioned, already recognizing that tireless wings are opening the whole world to wider markets, to a form of service that opens the sky to commerce.

How quickly the average man, startled for a moment out of the commonplace, sinks back once more into the routine of conventional activity. We have, for instance the arrival of Lebrix and Costes in New York, almost unnoticed. Yet what had they done? ...Across the Mediterranean they flew ...over the Atlas Mountains and above the burning gold of Sahara ...skimming the jungles of West Africa ...taking the long, breathless leap across the gray Atlantic ... high above the llanos of Brazil and the pampas of Argentina....and up, up, up and over the Cordilleras that look down upon the Pacific... along the backbone of the continent ... over the gulf of Mexico ... along the coast of the United States ... to land at last within sight of the skyscrapers of Manhattan.

This is not an epic flight. *Simply a preliminary survey for the French transatlantic airmail that will bring South America as close to French ports as California is to New York!*

But how quickly the exceptional man has realized the significance of tireless wings! We have, for instance, the *New York Times* delivered at the Pan-American Congress in Havana on the morning after publication. ... We have Armour and Company delivering packaged bacon in Detroit to meet an unexpected demand.... We have New York financiers and Los Angeles film producers gaining precious time... *all by the use of tireless wings!*

The Ford Motor Company expects as startling a development in the air as the present generation has witnesses along the highways. ... Thousands of brilliant minds are working on the problems that have hitherto hindered commercial progress. Neon beacons are piercing fogs! Radio telephones talk into the ear of flying man beyond the range of human vision! Earth inductor compasses point the way across the world! Radio beams mark highways through the sky!...

The tireless wings of Ford tri-motored, all-metal planes are yours to command!

FORD MOTOR COMPANY

FIRST TIME UP!

You settle back in your wicker chair a little nervously as the engines roar. Then a burst of speed across the flying field! Forty miles an hour . . . fifty-five! Someone shouts: "Watch the wheels !"

Unless your eyes are fixed on the great balloon tires no sense perception tells when you have left the earth. There is only an astonishing feeling of stability; then comfortable relaxation as the motors are throttled down. The giant, tri-motored car moves upward on a cushioning ramp of air....

Gradually you experience a sensation that is certainly one of the most extraordinary man has ever felt. You are transcending human nature. You feel immeasurably superior to the crawling beings in the miniature world immersed in silence two thousand feet below. Though you may suffer from fear of heights, this fear does not touch you now, for there are no lines of perspective drawing you earthward!

Streets, monuments, buildings, vehicles and living creatures are fractions of inches in size. Hedgerows, fences, and symmetrically plowed fields of red and brown earth form rug-like patterns, while distance gives the raw surfaces a velvety texture.

Boats, moving along a river the color of green onyx, push threads of cotton from their bows. Trains wind through the hills with lazy deliberation. Automobiles creep along ribboned roads. Sheep, cattle, horses, graze heads downward in the fields, unaware that you are watching from the sky.

The air of other-worldliness that hangs over the earth below is emphasized by the fact that you are hardly aware of forward motion, though moving twice as fast as the fastest express trains, and it is as easy to stand poised on one foot in the cabin as on the floor of your own bedroom. Your fellow passengers move freely about, shifting the ten wicker chairs companionably, to play cards, to typewrite, to make sketches, or, gathering in groups, first on one side of the plane, then on the other, to study the panorama below.

You soon accept the truth of the reported safety of these giant commercial planes. What if a motor fail? With two, the plane can continue to its destination ! If two fail—the remaining motor can extend the angle of descent to cover an area almost half the size of Delaware. And if all three fail the plane has a gliding range of miles.

Ford tri-motored, all-metal planes have demonstrated railroad efficiency for over a million miles of flight, carrying mail, freight and passengers . . . in tropical regions, in arctic regions, at sea level and over the highest mountain ranges on this continent.

Events of the last twelve months have put commercial flying in America on the level of stable industries. Great businesses have accepted it as a dependable means of swift transport, cutting two-thirds off railroad time. Business men no longer think of the mere thrill of "going up"; they think rather in terms of profitable service.

In the modern business world, the dawn of each new day presents a different scene . . . new products, new competition, new markets. To meet its challenge, you must be prepared.

When the occasion comes for your first time up, it will not be to "joyride" in an antiquated and hazardous machine; but far more probably it will be to reach some distant meeting-place in advance of business competition!

FORD MOTOR COMPANY

WHEN WOMEN FLY

Whose sympathetic counsel did the Wright brothers seek when studying the first principles of flight? Whose but their sister's! ... After Moisant won distinction in France, when France was leading the world in aerial pioneering, his pilot sister, too, added distinction to his name. ... How many men are today the equal of Ruth Law at the top of her fame? ... And when we speak of the brilliant flying of Eddie Stinston, isn't it only just to add that when Katherine Stinston was flying she was not only probably the most skilful woman pilot in the world but also at least the peer of most of the great men pilots?

Women do fly ... and fly well! Their share in aviation is already a positive one. Their contributions are of real value and their inspiration has undoubtedly been a factor in spurring men on to greater achievement in the conquest of the sky. ...

While man concerns himself with problems of engineering, and takes an artisan's pleasure in the mechanics of aviation and the organization of transport services, woman is swept aloft by the poetry of flight!

The spirit of modern woman is a free spirit that looks to the adventure of the skies with unreasoning exaltation. The spectacular drama and glamorous thrill of flight has caught her imagination. She may well picture herself as a Winged Victory or a dazzling Peri leaping into the empyrean while the world of fact sinks below in its clouds of dust and smog. See the part she takes in hazardous exploits ... endurance tests, stunt flying and aerial acrobatics, perilous flights and reckless adventuring! Or go sometime to such an airport as Cleveland's, where a hundred thousand people may be gathered to watch the colorful pageant of the sky ... and note the vivid part she takes there in the life and activities of the port!

Figures are not available to establish the proportion of women air-travelers compared to men; but a fair estimate of trans-Channel traffic from Croydon to Le Bourget puts the number at fifty per cent of men travelers. At the Ford Airport, and wherever Ford tri-motored all-metal planes fly in regular passenger service, women are insistent passengers, and, after their first flight, thrilled enthusiasts.

These unknown women ... tourists, business women, sightseers even ... who by their confident and delighted acceptance of aviation as passengers prove more surely than statistics that the world is adjusting itself to this new form of transportation.

For man no longer flies alone!

FORD MOTOR COMPANY

7

AVIATION ACTIVITIES OVERSEAS

The Ford Company's first, and what turned out to be their only significant, overseas aviation activities took place in England where in July 1929 they exhibited the 5AT-50 at the International Aero Exhibition at Olympia. Following demonstration flights in England, the Ford plane was taken on an extensive tour of twenty one European countries, carrying 3,750 passengers on 325 demonstration flights.

Two more planes, a 4AT-61 and a 5AT-68, were shipped to England in October of 1930 and with special permission of the Air Ministry were registered as G-ABEF and G-ABFF respectively ("F" standing for Ford).

5AT-50 on exhibition at the International Aero Exhibit at Olympia in England in 1929. (Robert Baron)

Interior of Ford hangar at the Ford Aerodrome, Yapton, England. Left to right, 5AT-107, 5AT-60 and 5AT-68. (William Larkins)

With the "EF" designation standing for Edsel Ford, they immediately started negotiations with the Air Ministry to change the "FF" registration to "HF" for Henry Ford. This apparently was no routine request as it took two months to gain their approval. The 5AT-60 was sent over at a later date as a company demonstrator. These planes were assembled and test flown out of Hooton Park Aerodrome, Cheshire, but needing a permanent operating location Ford officials found an old airfield at Yapton in Sussex, close to a small village coincidentally named Ford. Known as Yapton Aerodrome, the name was changed to Ford Aerodrome and would continue to be known by that name for many years after Ford ceased aviation operations in England.

Despite Ford's efforts, only two Tri-motors were sold in England and as a result of their European efforts, two were sold to CLASSA, the Spanish Airline, one to the Romanian government and one to the Czechoslovakian airline. One of the English units, 5AT-107, served with the RAF in World War II and reportedly took part in the 1940 evacuation of allied troops from Dunkirk. With the sale of the first plane to Spain, the German airplane manufacturer, Junkers, instituted a lawsuit against Ford claiming infringement on their patent **"wings with a corrugated skin"** and **"directly loaded wings."** The suit itself undoubtedly chilled Ford's sales efforts and when finally settled in Junkers favor in November 1930, it ended Ford's attempts to

Exterior of Ford hangar at Ford Aerodrome, Yapton, England. 5AT-68 is in front of hangar with 4AT-61 flying overhead. (Hudek)

penetrate the European aviation market.

The only other overseas sales effort occurred in February 1930, when James Bear, a Ford representative, along with Ford pilots Perry Hutton and Edward Hamilton, took a Ford Tri-motor, 5AT-65 to Yokahama, Japan. A letter dated September 10, 1930 from W. C. Cowling, a Ford executive in China looking for land for a factory, offers insight as to the conditions experienced in Japan and China. There had been no ground work laid for the exhibition and demonstration of the plane in Japan and the import permit had only been obtained two days before its arrival. No one had even asked the local Ford Manager for his advice. After a brief tour with no commercial interest being shown, **"it was decided as a last resort to send the plane to China."** Apparently, James Bear was blamed for the lack of success in Japan and was not included in the tour to China. In the course of demonstrating the plane it became a major concern that Ford not be drawn into China's internal politics by appearing to favor one side over the other in their civil war.

Reading left to right, LeRoy Manning and John Parker Van Zandt, Ford pilots and Carl Wenzel, Ford flight mechanic in 1929. They were on European trip to demonstrate the Ford Tri-Motor. Both Manning and Wenzel would be killed in separate crashes of Ford planes. Van Zandt was hired specifically for the this trip for $800 a month, and later would become an Assistant Secretary of the Air Force. (Robert Baron FMC 833.54200)

After one bombing raid on Peking (present day Beijing) the local press expressed the peoples' outrage in finding that 80% of the 33 attacking planes shot down had been imported from the United States. Cowling concluded, **"we have secured practically no benefit in the plane being over here."** This plane was finally sold in July 1931 to Marshal Chang Hsueh-Liang, Mukden, Manchuria who also purchased the 5AT-99 in February 1932.

STOUT METAL AIRPLANE COMPANY
DIVISION OF

Ford Motor Company

PERRY G. HUTTON   DEARBORN, MICHIGAN

Both sides of Ford pilot Perry Hutton's business card for trip to Japan and China in 1930. (William Larkins)

米國ミシガン州デーボン市

フォードモーターヂースタウト金屬飛行機會社所屬

スタウト自動車會社所屬
ヂードモーター金屬飛行機會社

8

POLAR EXPEDITIONS

The Detroit Arctic Expedition

In December 1925 the Detroit Aviation Society, under the Presidency of William Mayo, planned to organize and finance **The Detroit Arctic Expedition**. This was to be a trip to the North Pole for the purpose of exploration and crossing the Pole by air to demonstrate the existence of a short commercial air route over the top of the globe. Captain George Wilkins, a noted explorer, was to command the expedition and Lieutenant Commander Richard Byrd would be invited to be second in command. In February 1926, Edsel Ford contributed $5,000 to the expedition and it was planned that the new Ford

Tony Fokker would not sell a plane to Byrd for his Arctic Expedition unless he let Fokker plaster his name all over the aircraft. Currently on display at the Henry Ford Museum. (Hudek FMC 189.5391)

3AT Tri-Motor would participate in the expedition as a backup to two Fokker planes. However, the January 17, 1926 fire at the Ford airplane factory ended that plan. In a January 1926 letter to Edsel Ford, thanking him for his $20,000 contribution towards his own upcoming Arctic expedition, Byrd advised Edsel of his decision to decline the invitation by Wilkins. It proved to be a wise decision as Wilkins' two planes were damaged in forced landings causing the venture to run over budget and postponing his attempt. Wilkins, an Australian, was to accomplish his objective of a complete crossing of the Arctic polar basin in 1928 and receive many honors, including Knighthood from King George V, but by that time Byrd had made his epic journey over the North Pole. In December 1926, in answer to a request for additional contributions so the Wilkins' expedition could proceed the following year, Edsel Ford declined as he had committed his

Lt. Cmdr. Byrd's Antarctic plane 4AT-15, named the *Floyd Bennett* after his Arctic pilot. Currently on display at the Henry Ford Museum. (Hudek FMC 189.5984)

efforts and money to Byrd's Arctic efforts.

Richard E. Byrd - Arctic Expedition

Few people are aware of just how responsible Edsel Ford was for Richard Byrd's Arctic and Antarctic Expeditions. In March 1925, Admiral William Moffett, Chief of Naval

Aviation, had written Henry Ford to introduce him to Lt. Cmdr. Richard Byrd and his proposed trip to the North Pole stating:

"I think that Byrd has the ability and determination to succeed in this undertaking, and I want to assure you that you could make no mistake in putting the utmost confidence in him. He is the kind who enjoys life most when there are difficulties to overcome."

While the Navy aviation supported and encouraged Richard Byrd's proposed expeditions due to the great publicity value versus the Army aviation, the peacetime Navy had no funds to support it. Through his personal financial contributions and encouragement and solicitation of other prominent businessmen, Edsel Ford proved to be the underlying force in Byrd's ventures. In January 1926 Edsel Ford sent a check for $20,000 to support Byrd's North Pole trip and this contribution, along with one from John D. Rockefeller Jr. (after a letter from Edsel Ford), and one other from an unidentified supporter, provided the bulk of Byrd's financing. Byrd had hoped to use the new Ford 3AT Tri-Motor for his polar trip, but in February 1926 Ford wired him that the plane had been destroyed in the recent airplane factory fire. This left only the Fokker plane and in gratitude for Ford's assistance Byrd named the Fokker plane *Josephine Ford* after Edsel Ford's daughter. Apparently this caused Anthony Fokker to be concerned that the Ford name

would be more prominent on the airplane than his own, as Byrd wrote Edsel Ford on April 1, 1926:

"Mr. Fokker has written his name all over the plane, but I could not help that, as he said he would not sell it to me unless I allowed him to do so."

In an April 4, 1926 letter to Edsel Ford, Byrd wrote:

"The whole thing would have been impossible without your backing and encouragement. I owe a great deal to a great many people, but I owe more to you than all the rest put together."

Following the successful completion of the North Pole trip (May 8, 1926), Ford purchased the Fokker airplane for $30,000.

Richard E. Byrd - Antarctic Expedition

Edsel Ford contributed $90,000 in cash and materials to Byrd's Antarctic trip (November 30, 1929) and had again written letters to other influential people requesting their financial assistance for Byrd's new effort. Again, John Rockefeller came through with a contribution, this time for $50,000, although he asked Edsel to keep his contribution a secret. By then the Ford Tri-Motor was a reality and Byrd's only choice (considering Edsel Ford's backing), although he had ordered a Fokker before he was assured of

Front and back views of the 4AT-15 *Floyd Bennett* being dug out of the Antarctic ice in 1935. (Hudek)

the Ford plane being available. In September 1927 Byrd informed Edsel Ford that he had tried to cancel the Fokker he had ordered but that Fokker refused:

"Fokker and Llorillard Spencer, President of the Company, admitted to me in New York the other day that should I use a Ford plane it would be a terrible blow to them.

I have put Fokker on the map in this country and now he won't do me the courtesy to cancel the contracts I have made with him, even though he admitted that he had more orders than he could possibly fill."

The Ford Tri-Motor 4AT15, used in this expedition, was named the *Floyd Bennett* in memory of Byrd's deceased arctic expedition pilot. It was built with celluloid windows, thinner gauge skin for the fuselage and parts of the wings to reduce weight and tanks for 745 gallons of gas (vs normal 235 gallons). In addition, the 220hp Wright Whirlwind center engine was replaced with a 525hp Wright Cyclone engine with a three bladed prop. The plane was left behind, buried in the ice and snow until 1935 when Byrd returned to the Antarctic and retrieved it. While the plane was well preserved in the ice, a great deal of damage was done to the thin skin of the plane in digging it out of the snow and chipping off the ice. It was returned to Floyd Bennett Field, Long Island, NY in August 1935 by the merchant ship, *SS Jacob Ruppert*. It was completely dismantled, packed in 25 crates, and transshipped on the Ford canal boat, *MS Edgewater,* arriving in Dearborn September 6, 1935. It was restored by the remaining slim crew at the Airplane Division and placed on display in the Henry Ford Museum where it is currently housed along with Byrd's Arctic Fokker airplane, the *Josephine Ford*. In December 1929 Byrd was advanced to the rank of Admiral by a special act of Congress.

While the Fords certainly participated in these ventures from a civic sense, they also undoubtedly sensed the publicity value of a successful expedition. Certainly the publicity surrounding the Arctic Expedition led to their much greater involvement in the antarctic expedition.

As a result of Ford's apparent success in his aviation venture (certainly emphasized by Byrd's Antarctic flight), General Motors was probably persuaded that the aviation field was too important to ignore. Their General Aviation Corporation, among other aviation investments, gained control of Fokker's American operation just in time for Knute Rockne's death in the crash of a Fokker Tri-Motor in 1931. By 1935 General Motors was out of the aviation business.

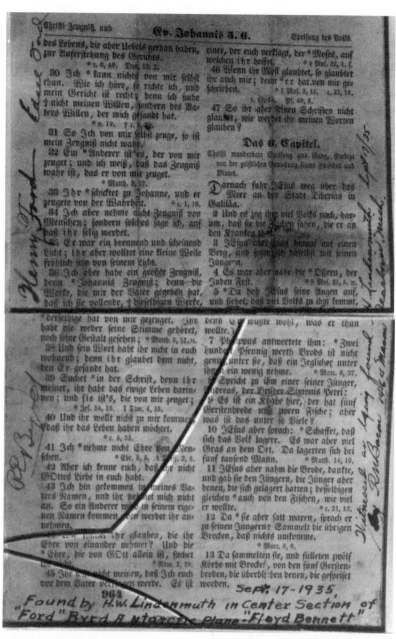

Page from German bible found hidden in Byrd's Ford plane the *Floyd Bennett* after it was returned from the Antarctic in 1935. Signed by Richard Byrd, Henry and Edsel Ford, and signatures attested to by Robert Barron. (Jon Aldrich)

9

EXPERIMENTAL PLANES

Ford engineers not only experimented with all sorts of engine combinations for the big Tri-motor planes, looking for improved power and performance, but also developed a number of other very distinct aircraft.

1926	Single seat, low wing *Flivver* with 3 cylinder Anzani engine.
1927	Two seat, twin engine amphibian.
1927	Five seat, single engine, high wing monoplane.
1927	Single seat, low wing *Flivver* with two cylinder Ford engine.
1929	Single engine freighter, modified 5AT (8AT).
1930	Tri-Motor with outboard engines buried in wings (5AT8O).
1931	XB906 Bomber, modified 5AT.
1932	32 passenger, low wing tri-motor transport (14AT).
1932	14 passenger, low wing twin engine transport (15AT).
1936	Two seat, flying wing, with souped up Ford V8 engine (15P).

Flivver # 1

The existence of the Ford single seat *Flivver* had been rumored for some time but not made official until July 30, 1926 on the occasion of Henry Ford's usual birthday interview with newspapermen. It had been glimpsed in test flights around Ford Airport for several weeks, having been built June 8th, but like many of Ford's projects, confirmation was difficult to come by until Henry Ford was ready to do so. It was first publicly demonstrated at the start of the Ford Reliability Air Tour on August 7, 1926. It generated a great deal of press attention and while most of the press and public hailed this plane as the Model T of the air, a plane for the masses, the *Grand Rapids Press* (MI) was less ecstatic, stating:

"A sturdy little Ford plane, put on the market, say at $498, fully equipped with standard gear shift and balloon tires, would be a national menace. The longer American aviation remains in the hands of the large common carrier, instead of the private pleasure adventurer, the better all around."

Ford publicly denied any intentions of mass producing the *Flivver*.

Ford *Flivver #1* with three cylinder Anzani engine. Currently hanging in Henry Ford Museum. (Hudek FMC 189.4233)

Henry Ford looking on as Charles Lindbergh gets briefing from Ford pilot Harry Brooks prior to testing *Flivver #1*. (Hudek FMC 833.49740)

Harry Brooks in *Flivver #1* buzzing Navy's airship *Los Angeles* (Hudek)

The plane was designed by Otto Koppen, a recent graduate of MIT. It consisted of a fabric covered wooden frame 16 feet long with a wing span of 21 feet 9 inches, weighing 320 pounds. While the plane was powered by a three cylinder Anzani air cooled engine, developing 35hp and a top speed of 85 mph, Ford had announced at the *Flivver's* unveiling that Ford engineers were already working on a 2 cylinder replacement engine. In any event, it was a quick, nimble craft as demonstrated in a Ford motion picture film of the period showing it getting off the ground in about three seconds! This film also shows Harry Brooks, Ford's Chief Test Pilot, actually flying the *Flivver* over, under and around the Army's airship *RS-1* and the Navy's airship *Los Angeles*. With the crash of the Navy's *Shenandoah* the previous year and the potential for disaster this casual flying posed, it is hard to imagine that more severe safety rules weren't enforced. The plane was only flown by Brooks and by Charles Lindbergh on the occasion of his visit to Ford Airport in August 1927. The plane was completely restored in 1981 by the Detroit Institute of Aeronautics at a cost, for materials only, of $2,068 and currently hangs in the Henry Ford Museum in Dearborn, MI.

Two Seat Amphibian

With the success of the 4AT, Henry Ford apparently softened his attitude towards Stout, for in April 1927 Stout designed and built an all metal, two seat, twin engine, tandem wing amphibian. The plane was powered by a pair of 4 cylinder Bristol Cherub engines that they could never get to run properly. It was taxied once by Leonard Flo, hitting a bump at 70 mph, bouncing ten feet in the air and collapsing the landing gear on impact. One of the engines was salvaged for use in a small one seat vehicle built for Henry's grandsons. All that is known about this plane is in the notes of Robert Baron and the oral histories of Bill Stout and Harold Hicks, Chief Design Engineer of the Airplane Division. There is no record of it having received an experimental registration from the Department of Commerce.

Five Seat Executive Monoplane

In light of the wreck of the twin engine amphibian, it is fortunate that this plane, also designed by Stout, was being built at the same time in April of 1927. It was an all metal, five seat high wing monoplane powered by a Wright Whirlwind J-5 engine of 225hp with a wingspan of 45 feet and a gross weight of 3,700 pounds. It was a serious attempt by Ford to enter the executive/recreation market as evidenced by an article in the *Ford News* for June 22, 1927 and an interview with Mayo in the *Automotive Industries* magazine for September 24, 1927. Unfortunately, it didn't fly very well. The engine was not placed far enough forward to give it proper balance and pilot Eddie Hamilton declared after the test flight, **"I think you should run a band saw through it before you kill some-**

Two seat, twin engine, amphibian designed by Stout in April 1927. Bill Stout is standing on the left. It was not a successful design. (Hudek FMC 189.4281)

Another view of Bill Stout's twin engine amphibian. (Hudek FMC 189.4279)

Five seat executive plane designed by Stout in April 1927. It wasn't successful either. (Hudek FMC 189.4652)

Rear view of Stout's five seat executive plane. (Hudek FMC 4653)

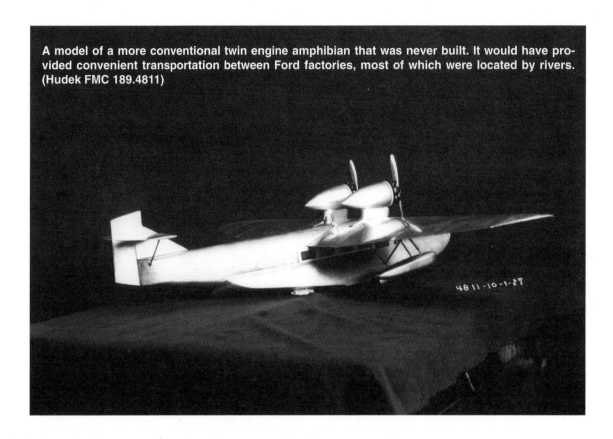

A model of a more conventional twin engine amphibian that was never built. It would have provided convenient transportation between Ford factories, most of which were located by rivers. (Hudek FMC 189.4811)

body." License number X-1085 was issued August 1, 1927 and cancelled February 15, 1929. No other information has been found on this plane.

Flivver #2

With the aviation craze generated by Lindbergh's historic Atlantic flight in 1927, everyone wanted to break records, and it was undoubtedly a major motivating factor in building *Flivver #2*. This plane was built to break the world's existing light plane distance record of 870 Miles. Otto Koppen also designed this plane, probably with substantial kibitzing from Harry Brooks, and it was introduced to the public at the start of the Gordon Bennett International Balloon Race on September 10, 1927. To the casual observer these two planes seemed similar, but number 2 was quite different. It was a larger plane, with a fabric covered steel frame and was powered by a new two cylinder engine designed by Harold Hicks that developed 29hp and a top speed of 90 mph. This plane was 16 feet, 6 inches long with a wing span of 25 feet and weighed 550 pounds empty. *Aviation* magazine for Feb 27, 1928 stated, **"it has carried more than its own weight and carries the same load, in proportion to its** lifting surface, as the most efficient large plane." There were at least five different configurations of the two Flivver planes using the two engines and different wing arrangements. On January 25, 1928 Harry Brooks took off from Ford Airport, Dearborn, MI in *Flivver #2*, heading for Miami in an attempt to break the world Class "C" light plane record. Nine hours and 500 miles later he was forced down in Emma, NC by bad weather and icing. While he hadn't set a world's record, he had bettered the US record of 472 miles. On February 21, 1928 Brooks tried again, leaving Ford Airport and flying nonstop to Titusville, FL, setting a new world

record certified at 1,564 kilometers (972 miles). This was quite a feat considering this flight was in an open cockpit in the middle of the winter. Unfortunately, four days later he crashed in the Atlantic ocean and although the plane wreckage was recovered, his body was never found and the cause of the accident never determined. The wreckage was returned to Dearborn and it has always been assumed it was discarded. However, accession records in the Henry Ford Museum state **"It was brought back to Dearborn, restored and placed in the Museum."** A later notation in 1951 indicates it was missing from the museum and a marginal notation

Ford *Flivver #2* at Ford Airport December 1927. (Hudek FMC 189.5107)

states "**Mr. D** [undoubtedly Ray Dahlinger] **had the plane destroyed."** In addition, Al Espers, a Ford engineer, states in his 1951 oral reminiscences, **"They brought back parts and put them together. I saw it when it was completed, and it looked the same as it did before it was cracked."** He further stated that it was in the museum at the present

Sure sounds like they might have rebuilt *Flivver #2*! What an intriguing mystery!

Henry Ford was very fond of Harry Brooks and his untimely death at age 25 was a blow. While there has been much speculation as to the cause of the crash, nothing definitive was ever established, but it did end Ford's experi-

Ford *Flivver #2* and Chief Test Pilot Harry Brooks on beach at Titusville, FL, after world's record breaking flight in February 1928. He died four days later when his plane crashed into the Atlantic ocean. (John Bluth)

time (1951). Also, John Dahlinger states, in his 1978 autobiography, The Secret Life of Henry Ford, **"After Brooks died in the plane, it was rebuilt and during the war kept at Ford Airport."** Dahlinger, who claimed to be the illegitimate son of Henry Ford, went on to say that he had flown the rebuilt *Flivver* with Henry Ford's permission.

ments with small planes until the 15P in 1935.

8AT Single Engine Freighter

At the peak of Ford production in 1929, Ford was looking ahead to expand, and the XB906 bomber for the military and the 8AT freighter for commercial use was an attempt to exploit

8AT was built on a 5AT frame with single Wright Cyclone engine and designed for freight use. (Hudek FMC 833.59086)

these markets. On July 30, 1929 Ford first flew the 8AT with a single Pratt and Whitney Hornet A engine in an attempt to develop a plane for pure freight use. The original 4AT had been developed with three motors to increase its dependability and convince the public of the safety of air travel. With the greatly increased power available with the new engines, a single engine plane became feasible especially in carrying freight where the image of safety was not a concern. The three Wright Whirlwind engines on the first 4ATs were rated at 200hp each for a total of 600hp, while the final engine used in the 8AT, a Wright Cyclone was rated at 700hp. For almost five years Ford experimented with about eight different engines, according to Bob Baron, introducing it to the public on April 9,1931 with a 600hp Hispano-Suiza engine, and finally settling on the Wright Cyclone. The 8AT had the same fuselage, tail and wing of the standard 5AT and a payload of 3,500 pounds. With two less engines the drag was reduced, making the plane slightly faster and less costly to maintain. Ford was serious about their **"Ford Express,"** advertising in August 1931 that, **"The time has come for freight to fly!"** Based on the knowledge gained in this extensive experimentation, they offered to retrofit older 4ATs to single engine configuration to extend their useful life as freighters now that the larger 5AT was the airlines choice for passengers. No 4ATs are known to have been altered. This was the only plane built and was sold to Pacific Alaska Airways May 31, 1934. In 1941, Avianca of Columbia wrote the factory requesting information on how to convert the plane to a tri-motor configuration. As all avia-

tion plans and drawings had been put in storage and there were no Airplane Division engineers left, there was no one to answer their question.

Tri-Motor With Engines In Wings (5AT8O)

This adaptation of a standard 5AT included two 300hp Wright J-6 engines buried in the wings and one 575hp Wright Cyclone in the nose. While top speed improved marginally to 140.5 mph, it was offset by an increase in

5AT-80 with experimental engine configuration. It didn't improve performance enough to warrant changing production line. Was later rebuilt as a conventional Tri-Motor. (Hudek FMC 189.7721)

Rare photograph of model of 5AT80 with engines in wings in wind tunnel at University of Detroit. William Mayo at lower right. (O'Callaghan)

the landing speed. It was converted back to a standard Tri-Motor and sold to National Air Transport.

XB906 Bomber

While Ford had sold planes to the Army, Navy and Marines, they were all for transport use. The XB906 was to be an effort to crack the military bomber market. It was a highly modified 5AT-D first tested April 7, 1931. It was 505 pounds heavier, with a top speed of 156 mph (6 mph faster) and could fly to 20,000 feet vs 16,100 feet for the standard 5AT-D. In addition, it had a rounded,

more modern tail and all control cables were located inside the plane. It was the only Ford Tri-Motor designed for a single pilot. The Army Air Corps tested the plane July 27, 1931 at Wright Field and in replying to a Ford query summed up their four page critique as follows:

"While the airplane had some excellent bombing characteristics, these were offset by a large margin due to the lack of rearward vision, inadequate angles of fire for machine guns and inherently poor aerodynamic qualities."

XB906 was Ford's attempt to crack military bomber market. Army Air Corps wasn't impressed and plane later crashed killing two Ford employees. (Hudek FMC 833.56183.1)

Interestingly, they indicated that a mock up of the plane Ford had earlier built with an open cockpit provided adequate rearward vision. In returning the plane to Ford, they encountered a storm at 12,000 feet. They first hit a strong up current and in trying to bring the plane under control the flying speed fell to 80 mph. They then hit a down draft and before the plane was righted, a speed of 205 to 210 mph was noted. Two comments on this trip worth mentioning are in a memo submitted to Mayo by S. H. Morse, a Ford engineer who was a passenger.

"Lt. Berry (the Army pilot) informed the writer that he was prepared to leave the ship when it reached the high air speed of 205 mph because he thought that something would give way.

The structure of the plane, in the writer's estimation was no doubt put to a very severe test during this flight."

This plane crashed September 19, 1931, killing Ford's Chief Test Pilot, LeRoy Manning, and his Mechanic, L. H. Garriot. The only official comment on the crash came from Mayo who said, **"The crash was apparently the result of a motor explosion while the ship was in a power dive."** Cost of developing this plane was $119,327.

14AT 32 Passenger

Henry Ford had been convinced since his acquisition of the Stout Metal Airplane Company that in order for aviation to be profitable, larger planes had to be developed; planes capable of carrying at least 100 people. In an interview with the *New York Times* in July 1927, Mayo was quoted as saying, **"I have devoted more than two years to the designing of a 100 passenger plane and a 1,000 horsepower air-cooled radial engine."** This, at a time when few planes even carried ten passengers. However, with the existing state of aircraft design this larger plane was not possible.

In 1930, with the success of his 4AT and 5AT and through discussions with Charles Lind-

Artist rendering of 10AT model equipped with four Pratt and Whitney Hornet engines. This model would evolve into the 12AT and finally the 14AT equipped with three Hispano-Suiza engines. (Hudek FMC 189. 8393)

bergh and other aviation pioneers such as General "Billy" Mitchell, Ford was convinced the time was ripe for a bigger plane. Bill Stout relates that when Henry Ford discussed the development of this large plane, Stout cautioned that it might be wiser to build a smaller plane first. Ford replied, **"No, I would rather build a big plane and learn something, even if it didn't fly, than to build a smaller one that worked perfectly and not learn anything."** In June 1930, the 10AT was designed, a 32 passenger plane to be powered by four of the new Pratt & Whitney Hornet engines developing a total of 2,300hp. One engine was buried in each wing with two engines (a pusher and a tractor) mounted on a pedestal on top the center section of the plane. Later drawings and models featured a single engine mounted on top as a tractor or a pusher (12AT). In all cases, the fuselage and wings of the 10AT, 12AT and 14AT were the same. It was the type and number of engines that determined the model number. Evidently, the decision to switch to the three engine 14AT powered by the Hispano Suiza engines was made abruptly. On October 27, 1931 Harold Hicks had submitted a patent application relating to the four engine version (10AT). Yet by December 1931, *Automotive Industries* carried an article on **"The mammoth Ford aircraft Type 14-A"** and a photo showing the three Hispano-Suiza engines. In any event, in a review of Ford Motor Company relations with Pratt and Whitney prepared for Henry Ford II in 1959, it is stated that Henry Ford became displeased

because Bill Mayo, Chief Engineer for Ford and running the Aircraft Division, was also a director at Pratt & Whitney. He felt there was a conflict of interest even though he had agreed when Mayo was hired that he could retain outside interests. He resolved the problem by ordering the switch to the Hispano Suiza engines. Harold Hicks claimed that Henry Ford had been displeased with Mayo for sometime, so the Pratt & Whitney situation was probably a continuation of earlier problems. Hicks states that the switch to the heavy water cooled Hispano Suiza engines reduced the payload by 2,700 pounds and caused the Bureau of Commerce to reduce the authorized passenger capacity to 10.

This plane was to **"rival the most luxurious forms of surface transportation"** according to the *Aero Digest* in April 1932. They went on to relate that the passenger compartments would be like Pullman cars with sections on either side of a center aisle. Each section (8' 11" x 6' 2") would have two facing double seats being convertible into lower sleeping berths. Upper berths would be stored at air depots so no added weight would have to be carried on daytime flights. There was to be a smoking compartment, two lavatories and a galley with call buttons located in each compartment. **"Cabin interiors are furnished in harmonious color schemes. The seat cushion is constructed of rubber inflated with air to give utmost passenger comfort."**

Power for the 14AT was provided by two 12 cylinder, 650hp Hispano Suiza engines bearing four bladed props mounted in each wing and one tractor mounted 18 cylinder, 1,000hp Hispano Suiza engine, bearing a three bladed prop, mounted on a pedestal on the top of the center section. The center engine caused 1929 Schneider Racing Cup and the carburetor floats needed adjustments. These three engines would consume a total of 121 gallons of gas per hour! A unique feature of this plane was the semi-retractable landing gear. The wheel struts were extended 48 1/2 inches for take off and then retracted in flight. When

14AT - Ford's 100 passenger dream. In reality a 32 passenger plane that cost over one million dollars and never flew. They did learn a lot from it, as many new assembly and manufacturing techniques were developed. (Hudek FMC 833.56854.7)

considerable difficulty as they could not keep it running. According to Baron, the difficulty was resolved when a Hispano Suiza representative determined that this *tractor* engine had been designed as a *pusher* engine for the at the gate, the wheels were retracted bringing the plane's door sill close to the ground for passenger access without the aid of a ramp. With the wheels fully extended, Baron said it **"reminded one of a giant monster**

ready to leap into the air." Unfortunately, no photographs have been found with the wheels in the extended position. Specifications of the plane were as follows:

Wing Span	110 feet
Length	80 feet 10 inches
Height (wheels up)	19 feet 6 inches
Height (wheels down)	23 feet 7 inches
Gas capacity	500 gallons
Cruising speed	150 mph

It was a serious attempt to build a larger plane as Ford advertised in March of 1932, **"When Larger Planes Fly - Larger Ford planes will lead the way."** According to Baron, total taxiing distance was less than a half a mile. In checking Ford records for information on an unrelated Tri-Motor accident, Baron states he came across a memo stating the cost of the 14AT had reached $1,044,000. The memo was dated before any of the components had been assembled! One of the reasons for the enormous expense was that parts for three planes were fabricated, but only one was assembled. In June 1933 Ford requested the Department of Commerce to cancel the license as the plane was being dismantled. Apparently, the only thing salvaged was the 1,000hp center engine mounted on a pedes-

15AT - A designers dream. Wind tunnel model in March 1932, months before the Douglas DC-1, forerunner of the famous DC-3, was designed. (Hudek)

tal which was reported to have been used on the test track to simulate gusty wind conditions as test cars passed by.

15AT (Wind Tunnel Model)

Some Ford engineers believed that if the original 10AT with the Pratt & Whitney Hornets had been developed, Ford would have been years ahead of other manufacturers. In fact, by August 1932 drawings (and a wind tunnel model) of a new model, the 15AT, had been prepared and was **"almost a dead ringer for the DC 3"** (which had yet to be designed) according to Hicks. It was a low wing monoplane with a length of 51 feet 6 inches, a wing span of 80 feet with a gross weight of 13,340 pounds and passenger capacity for 14 people. It had a fully retractable landing gear and was to be powered by two Curtis Wright V-1650 engines of 720hp each, with a projected top speed of 215 mph. Too bad it was never built!

15P Flying Wing

By late 1931, production at the Airplane Division of Ford had virtually stopped, although there was an unsold inventory of planes on hand ready for finishing to a customer's specifications. While the airport and repair facilities remained operative for many years, Ford was out of the airplane building business. However, in November 1933, Gene Vidal, head of the Aeronautics Branch, Department of Commerce (and father of famous author Gore Vidal) issued a press release headlined:

"Plan For Widespread Development Of Private Flying Through Volume Production Of 10,000 Low Priced Airplanes."

15P - A design model that was probably a result of Bureau of Aeronautics effort to stimulate production of low cost airplanes for the masses. (Hudek FMC 188.11051)

The release went on to state that there were 14,000 licensed pilots, 11,000 student pilots and 8,500 licensed aircraft mechanics in the United States and only 7,000 licensed aircraft, 600 of which belonged to scheduled airlines. Vidal's goal was an aircraft seating two people, built of steel alloy, fitted with an eight cylinder engine, and equipped with a geared propeller. It would have a landing speed of about 25 mph and cost between $700 and $800. With an operational Airplane Di-vision, diminished though it was, this prob-ably was too much of a challenge for Ford to pass up. There seemed to still lurk in Ford's mind the hope of an aerial *Flivver* for the masses and by September 1934 a design model had been completed, quickly followed by a full size mock up in January 1935. The combination of Ford and Aviation still made news, for on January 13, 1936 the *New York Times* featured a front page article, **"Ford Licenses Experimental Flivver Plane."** In

15P - A mock up of the two seater with dummy registration number in 1935. (Hudek FMC 188.11722)

15P - Built in late 1935, this was Ford's last attempt at a plane for the masses. The first flying wing, but with a six foot propeller and no tail, it was difficult to control. (Hudek FMC 188.15927)

response to the hundreds of letters in the file requesting information on this new plane, the Ford answer was the same - the release was in error and they were not considering building a small plane. The release of this information also caused a stir in the Aeronautics Branch of the Department of Commerce as a January 24, 1936 letter from the local inspector states, **"Ford Motor Company was considerably perturbed that the publicity broke before they were ready to make an announcement,"** and he requested guidance for the future. Ford's complaint must have registered as this same inspector renewed their license June 22, 1936 without inspecting the aircraft.

There have been no company records found bearing on the development of this plane, however oral histories, newspaper accounts and Department of Commerce correspondence build an interesting story of Ford's **"last fling"** in civil aviation.

With only four or five men assigned to the Airport for handling Tri-Motor repairs, service and other assigned duties, apparently Edsel Ford had them work on a two seat flying wing, called a bat-wing and given the designation 15P (P for personal use), a natural number progression from the last plane built, the 14AT. It is interesting that this was a two seater (side by side) as Bill Stout relates that when Henry Ford approached him with the idea of the original single seat

Flivver in 1926 he asked Henry, **"How could you teach anyone to fly it without killing him?"**

The plane, designed by Harry Karcher, an MIT graduate, assisted by Gar Evans, a Ford designer/draftsman, was made of steel tubing with fuselage covered in aluminum alloy and the wings covered with fabric. The following dimensions, which are approximate, were taken from tracings Robert Baron made in 1978 from the original drawings by Gar Evans in March 1936:

Wing span   34 feet

15P - Three quarter rear view of the "Flying Wing". (Hudek FMC 188.15928)

104

Overall length   14 feet
Height   6 1/2 feet

Power was supplied by a souped up 115hp, Ford V8 engine with a cast aluminum alloy block mounted behind the occupants with a drive shaft passing between them to a 2:1 reduction gear to the large six foot Gardner wooden propeller. It had a standard automotive radiator under the engine, which was retractable into the fuselage. It had two 15 gallon gas tanks mounted in the wings, giving it a cruising range of about 500 miles. The idea of using a nearly standard Ford engine was to allow an owner to obtain parts and repairs at any Ford dealer in the country and be quickly on his way.

The occupants were seated at the center of gravity and longitudinal control was activated by shifting their weight forward or backward. Lateral control was by conventional ailerons

15P - A close up of the souped up Ford V8 engine and cockpit. (Hudek FMC 188.15926)

and yawing was controlled by split rudders attached to the trailing edge of the wing tips adjacent to the ailerons. As can be imagined, there was a difficult problem controlling the plane due to the strong torque of the large propeller. There was plenty of lift to get off the ground but in spite of everything they could think of, they couldn't control its tendency to turn. After several short flights by Harry Russell, it was involved in an accident and reportedly destroyed.

However, in 1941 Emile Zoerlin, another Ford engineer states that Henry Ford told him to **"attempt to make a combination helicopter and standard plane out of it."** This was no sudden whim of Ford's for in 1928, L. S. Sheldrick, a Ford engineer states Henry Ford had them lay out **"opposed piston engines with multiple crankshafts, which drove propellers that would act in the horizontal direction as well as propellers in the vertical direction."** Also, in a 1928 interview with the *New York Times* he was quoted as saying, **"A way must be found so that the airplane can descend vertically, so that it won't need a 40 acre field."** A special 10 cylinder engine (5 cylinders opposed) was developed and three engines actually produced. After much experimenting, and in spite of Henry's insistence, the engineers could not make the conversion work and the plane never got off the ground. It wasn't until Charles Lindbergh saw the plane and agreed with the engineers that Ford finally let the project die.

Harry Russell, the Airport Manager and chief pilot requested License X-999 be assigned to the plane, a reference to the Ford racer that Barney Oldfield drove to victory in 1902. It was assigned license number X-999E by the Department of Commerce on November 29, 1935 and subsequently reregistered until January 1, 1937. The last plane to bear the 999E registration was the Fokker tri-motor that crashed March 31, 1931 killing Knute Rockne, the Notre Dame football coach, and sealing the fate of the wooden framed Fokker.

10

AVIATION COLLECTION, HENRY FORD MUSEUM

Henry Ford was an avid collector of Americana, especially as it applied to our way of life from the late 1800's through the early 1900's. This devotion, almost an obsession, resulted in the establishment of the Edison Institute, Dearborn, MI, in October of 1929, later re-named the Henry Ford Museum and Greenfield Village. The Institute was composed of 260 acres which was originally part of the Ford Airport. With his interest in Americana, it was only natural that he acquire airplanes along with stage coaches, automobiles and locomo-tives as part of his transportation collection. One of the most significant aviation related items is the Wright brothers' Wright Cycle Co. building in Dayton, OH which was acquired and moved to Greenfield Village in 1936. It was in this shop that the first successful air-plane was built and then assembled and flown at Kitty Hawk, NC by Wilbur and Orville Wright in 1903. In addition, the following significant aircraft have been added to the collec-tion over the years.

1909 BLERIOT XI. This monoplane is similar to the one flown by Louis Bleriot in the first crossing of the English Channel in 1909. In a 1928 letter, Bleriot-Aeronau-tique, the manufacturer, states that this plane was number 169, built December 7, 1909 and referred to as their Cross Channel type. Purchased by Henry Ford in 1928.

Engine:	3 cyl, 25hp, Anzani air cooled
Length:	25' 8"
Wingspan:	28' 8"

1915 LAIRD. Emile Laird was one of the early exhibition pilots and used this bi-plane in one of the first aerial **loop-the-loops**, quite a daring stunt for the times. In 1917, Katherine Stinson, sister of the famous pilot and airplane manufacturer Eddie Stinson, took this plane on an exhibition tour of China and Japan. Donated to the museum in 1936 by Emile Laird.

Engine:	6 cyl, 45hp, Anzani air cooled
Speed:	65-70 mph, maximum
Length:	19' 5"
Wingspan:	25' 4"

1916 CURTISS MODEL F Flying Boat. This biplane is similar to the one Glenn Curtiss developed in 1911 as the first successful flying boat. This plane was purchased by Henry Ford for Evangeline Dahlinger, who was in effect his administrative assistant for personal affairs, one of the first licensed woman pilot in Michigan and the wife of Ray Dahlinger, manager of Ford's farms and the man who "fixed things" for Mr. Ford. Donated to the museum by Ray Dahlinger.

Engine:	8 cyl, 150hp, Hispano Suiza water cooled pusher
Speed:	69 mph, maximum
Length:	28' 10"
Wingspan:	49' 10"

1916 STANDARD J-1. This type of biplane was used by the Army Air Service for primary training 1916-1918. Donated to the museum in 1938 by Ernest Hall.

Engine:	8 cyl, 180hp Hispano Suiza
Speed:	102 mph, maximum
Length;	28'
Wingspan:	45'

1917 CURTISS JN 4-D, JENNY. This biplane was the primary pilot training airplane during and after World War I. There were 2,765 of this model built, creating a great surplus of these planes following the armistice in 1918. This made them very inexpensive, about $100 used and $600 new, resulting in nearly every pilot, or would-be pilot, using them to barnstorm the country for many years, delighting a public recently awakened to the marvels of the air. It was finally grounded in 1928 by the new licensing requirements issued by the Department of Commerce. This plane is the Canadian version known as a CANUCK. Donated to the museum by Ray Dahlinger.

Engine:	8 cyl, 90hp, Curtiss OX-5 water cooled
Speed:	79 mph, maximum
Length:	27' 4"
Wingspan:	43' 7"

1920 DAYTON-WRIGHT RB-1 Racer. This high wing monoplane was test flown by Jimmy Doolittle, the leader of the bombing raid on Tokyo in 1942. It was designed by Milton Baumann and flown by pilot Howard Rhinehart, thus the RB designation. Specifically designed to participate in the Gordon Bennett Air Race of 1920, it was forced out after the first lap due to a broken cable. It was the first aircraft to utilize a retractable landing gear and a variable wing camber. Donated to the museum in 1940 by the University of Michigan.

Engine:	6 cyl, 250hp, Hall-Scott
Speed:	200 mph, maximum
Length:	22' 8"
Wingspan:	21' 2"

1926 FOKKER F VIIa-3m. This high wing monoplane was a single engine Fokker F VIIa modified by adding an additional engine under each wing and entered in the 1925 Ford Air Reliability Tour. It was purchased by Lt. Cmdr. Richard Byrd for his famous flight over the North Pole in 1926 and named the *Josephine Ford* in honor of Edsel Ford's daughter, because of the assistance he had given Byrd. The plane, made of wood and fabric, was a great success becoming one of the outstanding transport planes of the times until the all metal Ford Tri-Motor was introduced. This plane was purchased by Edsel Ford after Byrd's Arctic trip in 1926.

Engine:	Three 9 cyl, 200hp, Wright J-4
Speed:	118 mph, maximum
Length:	47' 10"
Wingspan:	63' 4"

1926 FORD FLIVVER. This was a single seat, low wing monoplane and represented Ford's first attempt to build a Flivver of the air. A slightly larger Flivver built in 1927 broke the small plane distance record in 1928. Unfortunately, Harry Brooks, the pilot, was killed in that plane several days later ending Ford's interest in small planes for several years.

Engine:	3 cyl, 35hp, Anzani
Speed:	85 mph, maximum
Length:	16'
Wingspan:	21' 9"

1927 BOEING 40-B2. This biplane was one of a fleet of 24 planes built by Boeing Aircraft Company, for their subsidiary Boeing Air Transport (later United Air Lines), for the first scheduled transcontinental service between San Francisco and Chicago. The pilot was located in an open cockpit behind an enclosed, two passenger compartment and nearly 1,000 pounds of mail. It was donated to the museum in 1940 by United Air Lines.

Engine:	9 cyl, 500hp, Pratt & Whitney Hornet
Speed:	120 mph, maximum
Length:	33' 4"
Wingspan:	44' 2"

1927 RYAN NYP. This high wing monoplane is an original Ryan monoplane patterned on the *Spirit of St. Louis* and built after Lindbergh's successful crossing of the Atlantic Ocean in 1927. It was refurbished to the original *Spirit of St. Louis* specifications and used in the movie **"The Spirit of St. Louis,"** staring James Stewart in 1957. Charles Lindbergh inspected the plane after it was rebuilt and, according to Mr. Stewart, **"he approved everything we had done"** to replicate his plane. Donated to the museum by James Stewart in 1957.

Engine:	9 cyl, 220hp, Wright Whirlwind J-5
Speed:	112 mph, cruising
Length:	27' 8"
Wingspan:	46'

1927 STINSON, SM-1 DETROITER. This high wing monoplane was purchased by Edward Schlee, President of Wayco Oil Company in Detroit, named the *Miss Wayco* and entered in the 1927 Ford Reliability Air Tour with its builder, Eddie Stinson, as pilot. In finishing in first place it so impressed Schlee that he renamed the ship *Pride Of Detroit* and, with his pilot, William Brock, attempted a round-the-world flight in October 1927, just five months after Lindbergh had completed his epic flight across the Atlantic. Heeding the pleas of family and friends, they declined to attempt the flight across the Pacific and ferried the plane from Tokyo to San Francisco. Everything considered, it was still an outstanding performance. This plane was one of the most famous light aircraft produced from the mid 1920's to the mid 1930's. It was purchased by the museum in 1932.

Engine:	9 cyl, 200hp, Wright Whirlwind J-5
Speed:	113 mph, cruising
Length:	32' 8"
Wingspan:	46' 8"

1928 STINSON, SM-1DX DETROITER. This plane, a duplicate of the preceding plane, served as a test bed for the Packard diesel airplane engine. It made the first flight of a diesel powered aircraft on September 18, 1928. William Mayo flew in the plane in November 1928, undoubtedly leading to the building of the diesel powered Ford 11AT in April 1930. While more fuel efficient than comparable gas engines, it proved unreliable and under powered for larger planes. It was donated to the museum in 1935 by the Packard Motor Car Corp.

Engine:	9 cyl, 225hp, Packard diesel
Speed:	110 mph cruising

1928 FORD 4AT-B. This high wing monoplane was used by Richard Byrd in his historic trip over the South Pole in 1929. There were numerous modifications to the standard 4AT-B, primarily to increase power and fuel capacity and to reduce weight. It was named the *Floyd Bennett* after Byrd's North Pole pilot who had died while participating in the rescue of the *Bremen* flyers. It was placed in the museum after being recovered from the South Pole in 1935.

Engine:	Two 9 cyl, 220hp, Wright Whirlwind, One 9 cyl, 520hp, Wright Cyclone
Speed:	128 mph, maximum with three Whirlwinds
Length:	45' 8"
Wingspan:	74'

1928 JUNKERS W 33. This low wing monoplane is covered in corrugated duralumin (as is the Ford Tri-Motor). Named the *Bremen* after the famed transatlantic ocean liner, this plane was used in the first east-west crossing of the Atlantic in April 1928. It was more demanding than Lindbergh's flight the previous year as they had to fight the headwinds which, as tailwinds, had benefited Lindbergh. In completing their trip they made a forced landing on Greenly Island, Labrador, requiring a rescue flight organized by Lt. Cmdr. Richard Byrd and his pilots, Floyd Bennett and Bernt Balchen, using one of Ford's Tri-Motor planes. The *Bremen* was donated to the Museum of The City of New York by Baron von Huenefield, one of the three fliers. Lacking funds, the New York museum donated the plane to the Henry Ford museum in 1936.

Engine:	6 cyl, 310hp, Junkers L-5
Speed:	97 mph, cruising
Length:	34' 6"
Wingspan:	58' 3"

1929 LOCKHEED VEGA 5B. A high wing monoplane, this type of plane holds more overland and overseas records than any other type plane, with one being flown by Wiley Post in his round-the-world solo flight in 1933. This plane was initially used as a demonstrator by Lockheed and its log book includes such names as Charles Lindbergh and Amelia Earhart. It was used by Rear Admiral Donald McMillan in 1931 for one of his many Arctic trips for a survey expedition of Labrador and Greenland, mapping 50,000 square miles of additional terrain. Purchased by the museum at auction in 1968.

Engine:	9 cyl, 300hp, Pratt & Whitney Wasp Jr.
Speed:	160 mph, maximum
Length:	27' 6"
Wingspan:	41'

1931 PITCAIRN PCA-2. The first American autogiro built for commercial use, designed by Juan de la Cierva of Spain, was delivered to *The Detroit News* in February 1931. A major problem was encountered in licensing the craft as the Department of Commerce had no precedents on which to base its approval. Donated to the museum in 1934 by William Scripps, President of the *Detroit News*.

Speed:	123 mph, maximum
Wingspan:	20' 1"
Rotor:	45' 10" diameter

1939 DOUGLAS DC-3. This low wing monoplane logged 84,875 flying hours, more than any other single commercial aircraft in history. Replacing the Ford Tri-Motor as the aircraft of choice for passenger airlines, more than 10,000 were built. It formed the backbone of military air transportation in World War II under the designation C-47 and was affectionately called the *Gooney Bird*. It was retired from service and donated to the museum in 1975 by North Central Airlines.

Engine:	Two 9 cyl, 1,000hp Wright Cyclone
Speed:	180 mph, cruising
Length:	64' 6"
Wingspan:	95'

1939 VOUGHT-SIKORSKY VS 300A. This helicopter had a range of 75 miles and could carry a 250 pound load to an altitude of 4,000 feet. This was the first practical helicopter in the United States and, using a 90hp Franklin engine, established a world's endurance record in 1941 by remaining in the air for one hour and 33 minutes. It was donated to the museum in 1943 by Igor Sikorsky.

Engine:	4 cyl, 75hp, Lycoming O-134-C
Speed:	70 mph, maximum
Length:	27' 11"
Rotor	30' 2" diameter

1946 PIPER CUB J-3. This high wing monoplane was the Model "T" of the air, with over 30,000 built between 1931 and 1947 with virtually no engineering changes. The plane sold for under $1,000 in 1941. More US pilots learned to fly in this type airplane than any other. Donated by the Piper Aircraft Corporation to the museum in 1961.

Engine:	4 cyl, 65hp, Continental A65-8
Speed:	87 mph, maximum
Length:	28' 8"
Wingspan:	34' 7"

11

WILLIAM STOUT, WILLIAM MAYO AND HARRY BROOKS

No recitation of Ford and aviation would be complete without a brief mention of Bill Stout who claimed, **"In my opinion, the greatest single thing I accomplished for aviation was getting Mr. Ford interested in it. From that moment on, Wall Street and the country began to take aviation seriously."** Also a sketch of Bill Mayo, the man who ran the Ford Airplane Division, and a short history of Harry Brooks, is appropriate considering his closeness to Ford aviation and Henry Ford.

William Bushnell Stout (1880 - 1956)

Bill Stout, although never completing college, was very likable and an innovative inventor, designer, promoter and, most of all, the consummate salesman. With a fascination for aviation, he covered air meets for *The Chicago Tribune* and was one of the founders of the aviation magazine *Aerial Age*. His first "hands on" aviation job was in charge of production of the Liberty engine at the Aircraft Division of Packard Motor Car Co. in 1917 although he disclaimed any connection with its design. As a result of these efforts he was called to Washington as a Technical Advisor

to the US Aircraft Board during World War I. He later formed the Stout Engineering Laboratory, building several small planes including the first all metal plane in the US for the US Navy in 1922. His contract with the Navy was cancelled when a Marine pilot crashed the plane during the final acceptance test. The Navy plane was followed by the small Air Sedan (or AS-1) in 1923, which was the first attempt at an all metal plane for commercial use. Under powered by a 90hp Curtis OX 5 engine it was quickly changed for a 150hp Hisso. While it was not a commercial success, it did prove the practicality of an all metal plane. All of his planes carried the thick, internally braced wing with no external spars or guy wires. Walker, Mayo's secretary, afraid that an imminent rupture between Henry Ford and Stout after the 3AT fiasco would hurt Stout and aviation, claims to have engineered Stout's leaving by convincing him that he could accomplish more as an outside consultant, free to work on his own projects. Stout severed all official connections with Ford in March 1930.

After establishing the Stout Air Service be-

William Bushnell Stout, May 1929. (Hudek)

Owens-Rentschler Company of Hamilton, OH in 1913 when he designed and installed a giant tandem engine using gas and steam to generate power at Ford's new Highland Park plant powerhouse, a feat many experts said wouldn't work. This so impressed Henry Ford that he spent the next several years in persuading Mayo to come to work for him as chief plant engineer.

In 1916 Mayo finally agreed to work for Ford, but on his own terms. He obtained the right to retain outside business interests, including connections with his former company. Mayo was the only executive brought into the Ford Motor Company at this level and probably the only Ford employee ever allowed to retain outside business ties. By 1929 he was a member, or officer, of 17 aviation related organizations or businesses and a member of at least 20 other civic and local organizations. Mayo also had the title of Chief Engineer when virtually no one had a title in the Ford Motor Company, and during his years as head of the Airplane Division, he was allowed to garner unheard of personal publicity when others were being fired for the same thing. *Aero Digest* magazine stated in May 1931 that evidence of Henry Ford's genius was giving Mayo his opportunity in aviation and ended

tween Ford Airport in Dearborn and Grand Rapids, MI in 1926 as the first scheduled passenger line in the US, he was brought out in 1928 by NAT, later purchased by United Airlines. NAT did not purchase Stout Air Service because Stout had such great equipment or routes but because they were the first to develop the detailed business of running a commercial airline. NAT purchased an idea.

William Benson Mayo (1866 - 1944)

Mayo was Vice President of the Hooven-

Professor Hugo Junkers (left) and William Mayo at Ford Airport May 1928. In June 1928, the Fords rejected a proposal by Junkers for cooperating on technical problems. In December 1929, Junkers successfully sued Ford over the use of corrugated metal in airplane construction, effectively halting the sale of Ford Tri-Motors in Europe. (Henry Ford Museum FMC 189.5578)

the tribute to Mayo with, "**If American air transport has a father, that father is named Mayo.**"

As early as 1922 Stout, Mayo and Edsel Ford were members of the Aircraft Development Corporation and Mayo was the single most influential person in the Fords' recognition of Stout's aviation ability and potential.

After Frederick Rentschler, Mayo's previous boss, formed the Pratt & Whitney Aircraft Company to develop a new radial aircraft engine, Mayo was elected a member of the board of directors and, as previously mentioned, Henry Ford later seemed to feel there was a conflict of interest. This, with all Mayo's personal publicity and Ford's waning interest in the Aircraft Division, probably fueled Ford's displeasure with Mayo and provided one more reason to sever their relationship in July 1932. A very typical end to

116

many of Henry Ford's senior executives.

Harry Joseph Brooks (1902 - 1928)

Who was this fellow Harry Brooks who was Henry Ford's favorite pilot?

Harry Brooks was born in 1902, the son of Joseph and Mae Brooks, prosperous farmers in Southfield, MI. Like many boys of his generation, Harry was bitten by the aviation bug early as evidenced by his high school year book which listed The Sky Pilot as a book Harry would write. He was the typical All-American boy, participating in football and basketball and being voted the *Handsomest Boy* in his class while his girlfriend was voted the *Prettiest Girl*. On graduating from high school he pursued his interest by becoming a mechanic for a local airstrip owner for $20 a week and flying lessons. In those days a flying strip was anything from a cow pasture to a mowed hay field with a wind sock.

Harry soloed in Lansing, MI in 1921 and picked up spending money by carrying passengers for local hops around the Detroit area.

In 1925, Henry Ford, partial to fiddler's music, visited the Brooks' farm to listen to an "Old Time" orchestra whose fiddler was Harry's father. A plane Harry was flying happened to be on the front lawn of the Brooks' farm at the time and as Ford had just opened

Harry Brook's 1925 ID photo for certification as an air mail pilot. Pilots were not required to be licensed until 1927, however the US Post Office did require that air mail pilots have a minimum of 500 hours flight time. (Hudek, segment of FMC 189.3233)

his airport and was in the process of developing his airline, The Ford Air Transport Service, his interest in the mechanically inclined young aviator was natural. Harry probably reminded Henry of his own background; son of farmers, mechanically inclined, unassuming, yet self assured and a nondrinker and nonsmoker.

Henry took to young Brooks, hiring him August 11, 1925 for 62 1/2¢ an hour ($25 a week) working in the airplane plant. Six months later, in February 1926, he was appointed a relief pilot for Ford's Air Transport Service at $250 a month. Indications of Ford's interest in Harry are contained in an internal memo Schroeder wrote to Mayo on February 6, 1926, regarding Brooks' promotion, **"We have taken extra care with him, knowing the circumstances**." In November of the same year, when Edward Hamilton replaced Major Schroeder as airport manager, Harry was appointed as his assistant and Chief Test Pilot. In his first twenty one months as a pilot he would receive four increases by November 1927, raising his pay to $400 a month.

Further proof of Ford's fondness for Harry lies in the fact he was allowed to use the single seat *Flivver* airplane as his "company car," commuting between his home in Birmingham, MI and Ford Airport. This generated a great deal of local press, exceeded only by that received by William Mayo, the only other Ford employee allowed to receive any personal press attention.

You can readily understand Henry Ford's sense of loss when Harry crashed off the coast of Florida on February 25, 1928, in *Flivver Number Two*.

12

THE TERMINATION OF AVIATION ACTIVITIES

Peak monthly production of 25 planes, achieved in June 1929, was followed by the stock market crash in October of 1929, and only 34 planes would be produced in the next two and a half years. A July 1932 memo stated under the heading, "**Outlook for the next five years: We can build all the commercial trade requires for four years in about six months**." At the same time, Ford's automobile and truck production was plummeting from a near record 1,870,257 vehicles in 1929 to a 17 year low of 395,956 in 1932. With the bloom off the aviation business and the recession causing a disaster in the automotive industry, even Henry Ford with his immense wealth, had to concentrate on his core business. A contributing factor probably was the death of two Ford pilots and two flight mechanics in Tri-Motor crashes in 1930 and 1931. Ford's departure from aviation gave Boeing and Douglas the opportunity to design and produce modern aircraft that some say they were reluctant to do as long as Ford remained such a dominant force in commercial aviation. The introduction of the Boeing 247 and the Douglas DC2s and DC3s, made the old *Tin Goose* a tough sell to airlines in America, although they continued in service in many South American countries for the next thirty years. The last Tri-Motor was sold June 8, 1933, the airplane factory closed down and most of the men were laid off. A small repair staff was retained to service existing planes until December 1936 when all remaining men were transferred to the Rouge plant, returning as needed to fabricate service parts for Tri-Motor owners. Records indicate small parts were still being supplied to Tri-Motor owners as late as 1945.

The last notable aviation happening at Ford Airport was the October 23, 1934 stratospheric balloon ascent of Dr. Jean Piccard and his wife, Jeannette, for the purpose of studying the origins and nature of cosmic rays. The balloon was piloted by Mrs. Piccard, the first and only woman in the United States licensed as a balloon pilot and the first time any woman had piloted a balloon on a stratospheric flight. By reaching 57,979 feet she not only set a woman's altitude record but also became the first woman to enter the stratosphere. In addition to making the Ford Airport available for the ascent, William Gossett, a Ford radio engineer, developed a small VHF radio to provide ground to air communication for the flight. The decision to provide a radio proved providential as the sky was so heavily overcast for the 5 hour, 225 mile trip, which ended in Cadiz, OH, that at one point the Piccards thought they were over the Atlantic ocean. Due to weight limitations the radio was contained in a ten pound package but performed superbly, keeping the chase car in contact with the balloon to the point of descent where they witnessed the touchdown. The airport continued to function and it was actively used by the military, and later civil aircraft, until June 1947 when the new Ford Air Transport Office (organized in 1941 for flight testing the new B-24 bomber and executive transportation) was transferred to Metropolitan Airport at Romulus, MI. A propeller repair and overhaul department was maintained at the airport until mid 1948 when it was sold to Commercial Aircraft Inc. of

Rare set of ribbon badges used by officials, press and guests at the record setting balloon flight of Dr Jean and Jeannette Piccard at Ford Airport. Although the ribbons read September the flight was not launched until October 23, 1934. (O'Callaghan)

on a limited basis although a test track was laid out around the runways in 1938. In 1939, the CAA was advised, **"Planes arriving at this airport are instructed to circle the field twice. The automobiles will pull out of the way."** World War II rejuvenated Ford Airport

Willow Run, MI. It had been the only completely equipped propeller facility in the Midwest. This sale severed the last link between Ford Airport and aviation.

The mooring mast, which had been a Dearborn

landmark and had identified the Ford Airport for so long, was toppled October 26, 1946 and the terminal building was demolished on August 11, 1961. The hangar building and portions of the world's first concrete runway are all that remain of Henry Ford's venture, but they are still in use today for the engineering and testing of Ford products.

Ford had spent in excess of eleven million dollars on his aviation venture, running the first regularly scheduled airline in the United States for six years, building 211 aircraft of different types and sizes and convincing the American public of the safety, reliability and economy of commercial aviation.

Henry and Clara Ford watching the mooring mast being toppled, October 26, 1946. One of Henry's last public appearances as he died April 7, 1947. (Ford Motor Company FMC 833.83419.1)

Mooring mast being pulled over by cables attached to trucks in October 1946. The end of an era for Ford and the end of a Dearborn landmark. (Henry Ford Museum FMC B.111064)

Mooring mast on ground awaiting the scavenger's torch. (Ford Motor Company FMC 833.83419.10)

13

AVIATION WAR PRODUCTION

World War I

Aircraft Engines

Ford's main aviation contribution to the war effort was in the making of Liberty aircraft engines and cylinders designed by Packard Motor Car Company. Originally, the Liberty was an 8 cylinder 225hp engine, but when this proved to be impracticable for front line planes, the design was changed to a 12 cylinder 400hp engine. The cylinders were bored out of solid steel forgings which were laborious and expensive to make. Ford engineers devised a cylinder from steel tubing that reduced the labor and cost from $19.75 each to $8.25 each. Ford was to build 3,950 engines and 433,826 cylinders. Seven years later Ford would buy back about 40 of the engines he built for use in his single engine 2AT airplane.

Ford's other little known World War I aviation contribution was the development of an engine for a *buzz bomb*. This was a secret program that only became known forty years later, after World War II. General Hap Arnold directed a program to develop a low cost, long range, self guided, self propelled torpedo called a robot bomb, later known as the *Kettering Bug*. The missile was to be accurate up to 200 miles, carry a 200 pound war head and cost no more than $200. Charles Kettering, the famed General Motors inventor, was in charge of the project. Ford was charged with developing the engine. The engine, developed by Ford engineer C. W. Wills, was a four cylinder, 40hp, V-type engine weighing 151 pounds that could be mass produced for $40. It was mounted on a 12 foot biplane with a 14 foot wing span. Once over the target, the wings would fall off and the fuselage would drop to the ground like a bomb. The robot bomb was perfected in August 1918 and General Arnold went to France to develop the launch teams. He fell sick with the flu and by the time he recovered, peace was at hand. The project was not pursued further until the beginning of World War II when it was decided that pilots flying B-17 and B-24 bombers would be more accurate and not as liable to injure civilians.

One last defense project, while not aviation

World War II

Aircraft

World War II employee factory badge for Ford Airport. (Actual size 1 7/8th inch). (O'Callaghan)

The most publicized war effort by any American manufacturer during World War II was undoubtedly Ford's B-24 *Liberator* bomber plant at Willow Run, MI. In January 1941, Edsel Ford and Charles Sorenson, Ford's production boss, at the request of the US Government, visited Consolidated Aircraft in California, to examine the possibility of building aircraft wings for their B-24 bomber. Sorenson relates in his autobiography how he watched men building the massive B-24 like Ford used to build Model Ns in 1906. Sorenson was sure the wing assemblies made by Ford would never fit the fuselages built by Consolidated. Their planes were literally

World War II employee factory badge for Willow Run. (Actual size 1 7/8th inch). (O'Callaghan)

related, did hint at the future. It was Ford's decision to build submarine chasers, called *Eagle Patrol Boats* for the Navy. Ford built an immense factory at the Rouge to turn out these 200 foot, 615 ton steel boats on an assembly line basis. Nobody had ever produced boats of this size in such a manner. On January 18, 1918 the Navy authorized Ford to proceed with building these boats and in six months a building was erected, tools obtained and set up, men trained and the first boat launched July 11th in 1918. People shouldn't have been surprised when Ford proposed to do the same thing with airplanes 23 years later.

hand built and it would be nearly impossible to mate them to the precision manufactured Ford wings. Backed by Edsel Ford, Sorenson stated, **"We'll make the complete plane or nothing at all,"** and countered with a plan to build the entire bomber based on the precision automotive assembly line methods Ford had pioneered. Ford claimed they could build 540 bombers a <u>month</u> versus Consolidated's very ambitious goal of 350 a year. The plan was accepted and Ford's problems started.

Consolidated, while welcoming Ford's participation as a subcontractor, was wary (as were the other major airplane manufacturers) about Ford's entrance into the aviation field and its implication for postwar competition. They were not happy that Ford was to build the whole plane, but took the attitude

President Franklin Roosevelt visiting the Willow Run plant in September 1942. An uncomfortable Henry Ford is in the middle with Charles Sorenson, Ford's Production boss on the right. (Hudek)

General "Hap" Arnold, Chief of the Army Air Corps, with Henry Ford at Willow Run, July 1944.

that they would teach Ford how to build airplanes. Ford men, having seen how Consolidated built planes by hand, took the attitude that they were going to demonstrate how to build planes better and faster. The first Ford hurdle was in getting a set of plans from Consolidated. Up to date, detailed plans did not exist! Ford had to send their own engineers and draftsman to make a complete set. Ford was making changes all the time, improving the process while saving time and money, but getting the Army Air Corps committees and Consolidateds' approval for every change proved frustrating in the early days. Ford needed frozen production runs to mass assemble planes and the Army Air Corps wanted to make changes as soon as a report came in from the front. Ford prevailed, making significant changes at predetermined timing with previous planes being retrofitted. This was so practical, that by the end of the war most plane manufacturers were doing the same.

Ground clearing was started in March 1941, at Willow Run, MI, on what was to be the largest factory in the world with 2.5 million square feet of floor space and an assembly line nearly a mile long. Like many other Ford buildings it was designed by noted architect Albert Kahn. It was built in an "L" shape to prevent the final assembly line running across the Washtenaw County line into Wayne County (and probably higher taxes after the war). Ford had owned much of the property since 1931 and had established Camp Willow Run there to help sons of dead and disabled World War I veterans to get a start in life. While the plant was finished in November 1941 it took ten more months for the first B-24 to be produced. By October 1941 however, while waiting for Willow Run to become operational, Ford was training workers and producing bomber subassemblies in

B-24 knock down kit for assembly by Consolidated and Douglas. Four 63 foot trailers were required to transport the sub-assemblies for each plane from Willow Run to Texas. (Hudek)

the old airplane plant at Ford Airport in Dearborn, MI.

Most people couldn't understand why it was taking so long for Ford to get going. They just could not comprehend the enormity of starting up a plant this size to build an item with 1,225,000 parts and held together by 400,000 rivets. However, when you consider the enormous amount of scarce, specialized machinery and fixtures needed to build planes in a way they had never been built

before and the need to hire and train over 40,000 unskilled workers (peak employment was 42,331 in June 1943 with a 15% absenteeism rate!), most of whom lived 30 miles away in Detroit and had no expressways to speed their way to work, coupled with the enormous turnover of people being drafted and others going elsewhere to work (in May 1943, a 56% labor turnover rate was reported for the prior eight months), you begin to comprehend the magnitude of the task. Then add labor troubles as Ford had just signed their

Eddie Rickenbacker, top World War I Ace, signing B-24 with Henry and Edsel Ford looking on. (Henry Ford Museum FMC 833.77388.3)

Assembly line was built in "L" shape to avoid extending plant into Wayne County, MI where taxes would be higher after the war. (Hudek)

Transparent model of B-24 with Henry Ford II, Louis Mayer from Chrysler and Ford executives L. Meade Bricker and K. J. Keller, April 1944. (Henry Ford Museum FMC 833.79673)

Henry Ford II signing off on the 8,000th B-24 in March 1945. (Henry Ford Museum FMC 0.16064)

Last B-24 number 8,685 on June 28, 1945. Henry Ford had his name taken off and let employees sign their names before shipment. (Hudek)

first, ever, union contract; stir in what must have seemed like daily manufacturing changes to a production process set up to produce the same identical item by the thousands, and you begin to understand why start up production took so long and to appreciate what Ford was finally able to accomplish during the war.

By January 1943, with only 56 planes built in all of 1942, the press was calling it "**Will It Run?**" But Ford had been building fuselages and sending them as knock down kits to Consolidated making it possible for them to build 1,142 planes. By the end of 1942 though, most problems had been, or were being, solved. January production was 31 planes, February 75, and March reached 104. Although improving, it still took until November 3, 1943 for Ford to build its 1,000th

Eleventh Pratt and Whitney engine built by Ford being packed for shipment in October 1941. (Hudek)

elsewhere and orders for Ford bombers declined. Willow Run was awarded the coveted *Army Navy E* for excellence in May 1945 and the final plane rolled off the line June 28, 1945. The final total showed Ford built 6,792 fly-aways and 1,893 knock down kits (parts shipped to Consolidated and Douglas for assembly), for a total of 8,685 planes.

One of the most important of Ford's contributions was the principles with which their production people had been indoctrinated. Any project could be analyzed and improvements made and that accepted ways were always to be challenged. With their manufacturing experience they felt they could do any job better, faster and cheaper. And, in fact, they did save the government money on almost every defense project they undertook. On the B-24s alone they had dropped the price from $238,000 in 1942 to $137,000 in 1944. With their highly automated machines and assem-

plane, but in 1944 they began producing production miracles. In March 1944 Ford produced 453 planes in 468 hours, nearly one an hour and nearly 6,000 planes were built in 1944! In late 1944, when Ford was gearing up to build 650 planes a month, US priorities changed to B-29 and B-32 production

15 person CG-4A glider built at Iron Mountain, MI. They were towed to Ford Airport by C47s. (Hudek)

bly line approach Ford produced 47% of all B-24s built.

In October 1941 the *Dearborn Press* quoted Henry Ford as saying, "**When the war is over we are going to retain the building we are erecting and construct airplanes on a mass production scale**." In addition, Henry Ford had discussed the possibility of building a large, four engine commercial transport with Lindbergh in early 1942. However, Ford declined to exercise their option to purchase the Willow Run plant from the Government following the end of the war when Henry Ford II told employees, "**The company regarded it as designed to meet a temporary need and just as expendable as a battleship**." To the obvious relief of their po-

tential aviation competitors, Ford never entered the postwar aviation industry, being absorbed with saving the Ford Motor Company from financial ruin.

Aircraft Engines

Ford accepted a contract to produce 4,000 aircraft engines and on September 14, 1940, ground was broken in the Rouge complex for a 1,286,344 square foot production facility to build the Pratt & Whitney R-2800, an 18 cylinder, 2,000 horsepower radial engine. Six months later the building was ready for operation and the first Ford built Pratt & Whitney engine came off the line August 23, 1941. Never the one to waste anything, Ford hooked the engine test cradles to the power-

Jet bomb engine for Navy's "Loon" missile was a copy of the German V-1. (Hudek)

house so that the energy of the engines being tested could be utilized. At the same time an Aircraft Engine Apprentice School was established to train employees and Army Air Corps and Navy personnel. As in other defense jobs, innovative methods were devised and they cut the time required to build each engine from 2,331 man hours in November 1942 to 905 by June of 1945. The Aircraft Engine plant employed 23,384 people, built 57,851 engines and also earned the *Army* *Navy E* for excellence. These engines were used in the Curtis C-46, Douglas A-26, Martin B-26 (and AT-23 trainer version), Northrop P-61, Republic P-47 and Vega B-34 airplanes.

In March 1940 construction began in Manchester, England on a factory for Ford to produce Rolls Royce Merlin V12 airplane engines. As in the United States, Ford was starting from scratch in finding employees and obtaining necessary machinery. However, in war time England the task was greatly magnified. They could not take qualified people from other plants and in the end women accounted for 43% of the employees. They turned in a magnificent performance! In setting up production, Ford engineers found the drawing tolerances for the Merlin engines to be much greater than Ford allowed for their automobile engines. Ford reworked the drawings to much finer tolerances and in June 1941, the first Ford built Merlin came off the line. Production targets called for 400 engines a month costing £5,640 each. By September 1942 the target was exceeded and, again due to Ford production methods, the cost dropped to £1,875. By mid 1944, monthly production was over 900 units a month at a cost of just £1,200. Over 30,000 engines were produced and not one failed the stringent acceptance tests of the Royal Air Force. Most of the engines were MkXX models used primarily in the Lancaster bombers and the Beaufighter, Defiant, Halifax and Hurricane fighters.

Gliders

In April 1942 Ford accepted a contract to build the 15 person CG-4A glider designed by WACO. The wooden plane was a natural, and a lifesaver, for the upper peninsula residents of Iron Mountain, MI as their plant (which had provided wood products for Ford cars) had lain idle since Pearl Harbor. Drawings received from WACO were only half size and when redrawn to full size were found to be full of errors. The first glider was produced at Ford Airport in Dearborn while the Iron Mountain plant was being set up and on September 16, 1942 their first glider was towed into the air for its test flight. Cut loose at 8,500 feet, it maneuvered for 45 minutes before landing and was promptly accepted by the Army. Production started in December 1942 with a planned production rate of four gliders a day, later raised to eight. Initially, the gliders from Iron Mountain were dismantled, boxed and shipped to Ford Airport in Dearborn, a most inefficient use of time and money. The solution was for C-47 cargo airplanes to snatch two or three gliders from the ground and tow them to Dearborn. In June 1943 they switched to building a larger 40 place glider, the YCG-13. Again, Ford methods halved the time for construction and reduced the price of the smaller glider from $21,390 to $12,159 and the larger glider from $62,200 to $30,300. One major innovation was the use of a gluing fixture that reduced drying time from eight hours to ten minutes. At war's end, 4,204 of the smaller gliders, and 86 of the larger gliders, had been built and this plant too, had earned the *Army Navy E* for excellence.

Jet Bomb Engine

Ford was awarded a contract in July 1944 for 25 prototype jet engines to be used with a robot aerial bomb, code named MX-544. These engines were designed to fly for two hours with enough power to drive the engine and plane with a bomb load at 400 mph. The first three engines built, designated PJ-31-1, were accepted by the Army Air Corps, negating the necessity of the other 22. These units were produced at the Rouge complex and led to a production order for 2,500 engines. 2,400 engines were actually produced and used to power three types of missiles: the Army Air Corps' JB-2 and JB-10 and the Navy's Loon, with the JB-2 and Loon being copies of the German V-1 buzz bomb. There is no information as to whether these missiles were used in combat.

Other Aviation Production

In addition to the above major items, Ford also produced 7,053 bomb trucks, 17,008 jettison gas tanks, 87,390 aircraft generators and 5,360 rate of climb indicators.

Korean "Police Action"

With the outbreak of the Korean war in 1950, the Air Force turned to Pratt & Whitney for R-4360, 29 cylinder radial engines for the B-36 bomber, but insisted that there be two sources of supply. Because of their close association with Ford in the late 1920's and early 1930's, and during World War II, they requested Ford be selected as the second supplier. Ford was to build aircraft engines in a vacant government owned plant in Chicago built by Chrylser in 1943 and last used by the Tucker Automobile Company. When built during World War II it had surpassed the Willow Run plant as the largest plant in the world. The first engine was completed on December 24, 1951 with first shipments to the Air Force the following March. Again, Ford was starting from scratch with untrained people and quality on the first Ford built engines required overhauls every 100 hours. But within two years, Ford engines were delivering 1,200 hours between overhauls. Production ended in 1954 with a total of 3,071 engines built. In addition, Ford made bomber wings in Kansas City and Ford engineers in Dearborn helped develop the M-39, a very sophisticated electric machine gun that was mounted on the F-86 jet fighters.

14

FORD AIR TRANSPORT OPERATIONS TODAY

Detroit Metropolitan Airport,
Romulus, MI

The successor to the Ford Air Transportation Service (ATS), which terminated in 1932, was the Ford Air Transport Office (ATO) formed November 11, 1941 in the Ford hangar at the Ford Airport in Dearborn, MI. A manager, Chief Pilot, seven pilots and three mechanics were hired to form the secret Test Flight Department in connection with the

Ford B-24 bomber plant at Willow Run, MI. In 1947, by which time they were operating as an executive transport, Ford ATO moved operations to an existing hangar at the Wayne County Airport in Romulus, MI (Detroit Metro) to take advantage of modern radio range and traffic control facilities. Ford Airport in Dearborn was closed for good. In No-

Grumman G21 *Goose*. First plane of the Ford Air Transport Office formed in November 1941. (Hudek)

vember 1962, Ford ATO relocated to a new 72,000 square foot hangar on the airport and currently operates from that location.

The first Company plane, obtained in December 1941 for pilot training and transportation, was a Grumman *Goose* G-21 Amphibian. By 1946, Ford ATO was operating a Beech C-45 and two C-47s (DC-3) purchased from the Army Air Corps. From this small beginning, Ford ATO has operated 34 aircraft of 16 different types over the years, the largest being a Boeing 727 jet liner from 1972 to 1974. They currently employ 24 pilots operating four Convair 580s and four Falcon 900 Tri-Jets. The aging 30 passenger Convairs, in service since 1959, are being replaced with new Fokker 70, 48 passenger twin jet aircraft.

With over 70 million miles flown, they have had only one fatality and that was in 1950 when a passenger was killed by an air conditioning unit that had broken loose from its mounting. In January 1994 they were awarded the National Business Aircraft Association safety award for 41 consecutive years and 183,146 hours of flight operations free of accidents. Ford ATO had the best combined record of any of the more than 3,000 NBAA members. The record was broken a few months later when the nose wheel failed to deploy on one of their Falcon Jets, leading to the discovery of a design defect in the plane.

Stansted Airport, Essex, England

With the consolidation of all Ford European activities under Ford of Europe there developed an enormous increase in personnel travelling between Ford's various marketing and manufacturing sites in Europe. Based on Ford's American experience the Ford Air Transportation Department was inaugurated at Stan-

50th Anniversary
Ford Air Transportation
Ford
1941 - 1991

You are cordially invited to attend
the Fiftieth Anniversary of
Ford Motor Company Air Transportation Office

May 15, 1992
Ford Motor Company Hangar
Middlebelt Road
Detroit Metro Airport
Detroit, Michigan

Reception ~ 6:00 PM
Dinner ~ 7:00 PM
Program ~ 8:00 PM

R.S.V.P. by May 1st, 1992 ~ 313-594-1308

sted, outside of London, on August 14, 1967 utilizing a hangar built by the US Army Air Corps in World War II. Starting with one Gulfstream G1 as a flexible flight service for senior executives, it quickly expanded, with the addition of additional aircraft, into a schedule service to many of the countries throughout Europe. In 1989, Ford moved into a new hangar complex at Stansted and the old hangar was removed and re-erected at the Imperial War Museum airfield at Duxford, Cambridgeshire. In 1987, *Fordair* was presented the Gold Award for Occupational Safety by the Royal Society for the Prevention of Accidents, a significant award for an air transportation operator. They currently operate one Gulfstream G1, one BAC 111 and two MD87s (modified DC9).

In April 1984 Henry Ford was enshrined in the National Aviation Hall of Fame in Dayton, OH, a fitting tribute to one of the great pioneers of commercial aviation in the United States.

15

ADDITIONAL INFORMATION

Ford Air Transport Service Statistics
April 13, 1925 - August 6, 1932

	Inaugurated	Terminated
Dearborn - Chicago	Apr 13, 1925	Aug 6, 1932
Dearborn - Cleveland	Jul 1, 1925	Jul 19, 1928
Dearborn - Cleveland	Mar 10, 1930	Apr 9, 1932
Dearborn - Buffalo	Mar 26, 1927	Mar 10, 1930
Cleveland - Buffalo	Mar 10, 1930	Jan 12, 1931

	DRBRN CHCGO	DRBRN CLEVE	CLEVE BUFLO	DRBRN BUFLO	TOTAL
Trips Scheduled	4,395	3,586	460	1,708	10,149
Trips Completed	4,115	3,435	420	1,473	9,443
% COMPLETED	94	96	91	86	93
Trips cancelled (mainly weather)	134	109	35	208	486
Forced landings:					
Weather	107	29	5	21	162
Mechanical	39	13	0	6	58

(30 of the 58 mechanical failures were with 2ATs in first two years of Air Transport operations.)

	DRBRN CHCGO	DRBRN CLEVE	CLEVE BUFLO	DRBRN BUFLO	TOTAL
Flying hours	10,644	4,799	805	4,055	20,303
Miles flown	993,108	444,222	84,711	356,344	1,878,385
Freight (000 #)	5,655	4,459	731	1,965	12,810

Air Transport 2AT Production
April 1924 - December 1925

	Name of plane	Purchaser	In Service
2AT1	Maiden Detroit	US Post Office	Dec 1924
2AT2	Maiden Dearborn I	Ford Air Transport Service	Apr 1925
2AT3	Maiden Dearborn II	Ford Air Transport Service	Apr 1925
2AT4	Maiden Dearborn III	Ford Air Transport Service	Jul 1925
2AT5	Maiden Dearborn IV	Ford Air Transport Service	Jul 1925
2AT6	Maiden Dearborn V	Ford Air Transport Service	Sep 1925
2AT7	J W 1	John Wanamaker Co	Oct 1925
2AT8	Miss Tampa*	Florida Airways #1	Dec 1925
2AT9	Miss Miami*	Florida Airways #2	Dec 1925
2AT10	Miss St Petersburg*	Florida Airways #3	Dec 1925
2AT11	Miss Ft Meyers*	Florida Airways #4	Dec 1925

*No records found to established Ford serial numbers of these planes.

There has been some question as to how many 2ATs were built and their serial numbers. A letter dated August 4, 1927, from Stout's office to F. L. Black, Ford Advertising, recapping planes produced to that date, lists planes with serial numbers 2 through 6 as purchased by Ford Motor Company, number 7 as purchased by the Wanamaker Company and numbers 8 through 11 as purchased by Florida Airways. The next eight planes listed are 4AT Tri-Motors, with the ill fated 3AT being conveniently forgotten. Ford purchase orders to the Stout Metal Airplane Company for the first four planes have been found and state these planes were the 2nd, 3rd, 4th and 5th serial numbered units and that number 4 was the *Maiden Dearborn III* and number 5 was the *Maiden Dearborn IV*. (Number 1 was the *Maiden Detroit* sold to the Post Office Department.) The only unknown is how many 2ATs in the process of being built, were lost in the January 1926 fire that destroyed the Stout Airplane factory.

Purchase Orders for the first two 2ATs placed in the Ford Air Transport Service. (Ford Air Transportation Office)

Ford Motor Company

ORIGINAL

HIGHLAND PARK, MICH.

This Order Number must appear on all Packing Slips, Bills of Lading, Machines, Packages and Invoices

The FORD MOTOR COMPANY, of Highland Park, Michigan, first party, hereby agrees to purchase and receive at its Dearborn, Mich., Plant, and

Purchase Order No. M 15854

Stout Metal Airplane Co Inc

7-6-25 192

Dearborn Mich

DELIVERY REQUIRED

second party agrees to manufacture, sell and deliver materials specified below, subject to the terms and conditions stipulated:

Delivered - do not duplicate

SHIP VIA   TERMS AT ONCE   F.O.B. Cars Dearborn

QUANTITY	DESCRIPTION OF MATERIAL		PRICE
1 only	Airplane "Maiden Dearborn 3" Serial #4	ea	$22,500.00
	Credit for Liberty Engine	"	$ 2,500.00
			20,000.00

FHD:EM
Inv 6-30-25
Memo
235-103

DEARBORN PLANT

Conditions

Acceptance:
Crating: Inspection:
Invoices:
Shipping Documents:
Packing Slips:
Statements: Cancellation:
Patents:
Freight Rate:

Ford Motor Company

Ford Motor Company

ORIGINAL

HIGHLAND PARK, MICH.

This Order Number must appear on all Packing Slips, Bills of Lading, Machines, Packages and Invoices

The FORD MOTOR COMPANY, of Highland Park, Michigan, first party, hereby agrees to purchase and receive at its Dearborn, Mich., Plant, and

Purchase Order No. M 15860

Stout Metal Airplane Co

July 21 192 5

Dearborn, Michigan

DELIVERY REQUIRED

second party agrees to manufacture, sell and deliver materials specified below, subject to the terms and conditions stipulated:

ALREADY DELIVERED -
DO NOT DUPLICATE

SHIP VIA DELIVERED   TERMS AT ONCE   F.O.B. Car Dearborn Plant

QUANTITY	DESCRIPTION OF MATERIAL		PRICE
1 only	Airplane "MAIDEN DEARBORN 4"	ea	22,500.00
	Serial No. 5		
	CREDIT FOR LIBERTY ENGINE		2,500.00
			20,000.00

FHD-EMH
Memo
235-103

DEARBORN PLANT

CONDITIONS

Acceptance:
Crating: Inspection:
Invoices:
Shipping Documents:
Packing Slips:
Statements: Cancellation:
Patents:
Freight Rate:

Ford Motor Company

By

Purchase Order No. M 15860

Purchase Orders for third and fourth 2ATs put in service. (Ford Air Transportation Office)

144

Ford Model Designations

2AT   Eight person aircraft, powered by single Liberty engine.

3AT   Modified version of 2AT using three Wright J-4 engines.

4AT-A Utilized three Wright J-4 engines. (Six other models used different engine combinations).

5AT-A Utilized three Pratt & Whitney Wasp engines. (Four other models used different engine combinations).

6AT   5AT airframe with Wright J-6 engines .

7AT   Modified 6AT with Pratt & Whitney Wasp engine in nose.

8AT   5AT airframe designed for single engine.

9AT   4AT airframe using three Pratt & Whitney Wasp Jr engines.

10AT   *Model* of 100 passenger ship using four Pratt & Whitney Hornet engines.

11AT   4AT airframe using three Packard Diesel engines.

12AT   *Model* of 10AT with Hispano Suizza in center mounted pedestal.

13AT   5AT airframe using two Wright J-6 and one Wright Cyclone.

14AT   32 passenger plane using three Hispano Suizza engines.

15AT   *Model* of twin engine passenger plane.

15P   Two seat, single engine flying wing.

Ford Aircraft Production by Year and Type
1925 - 1936

Year	2AT	3AT	4AT	5AT	8AT	14AT	X Planes	Total
1925	6	1						7
1926			2				1	3
1927			12				3	15
1928			38	17				55
1929			25	68	1			94
1930				10				10
1931			1	19*				20
1932				3		1		4
1933				2				2
1936							1	1
Total	6	1	78	119	1	1	5	211

Comparison Specifications:

	2AT	5AT	DC-3
Wing Span	58'4"	77' 10"	95'
Length	45'8"	50' 3"	64'5"
Empty Weight	3638#	7600#	16000#
Passengers	6	14	21
Cruising Speed	100	122	191

Ford's Aviation Expenditures

Land & depreciated value of buildings and equipment, May 31, 1932	$3,475,568
Inventory, May 31, 1932	1,266,242
Losses, 1925 - 1931	5,627,996
Estimated losses Jan '32 - Aug '33	1,000,000
Total	$11,369,806

Memo:

Land cost	$1,624,176
Purchase of Stout Metal Airplane Co	1,300,000
Mooring Mast	183,000
Cost of 14AT	1,000,000
Cost of XB906 bomber	119,327

FORD AVIATION PUBLICATIONS

Known Ford Motor Company Tri-Motor aviation publications.

Manuals
Book of Instruction, Ford All Metal Monoplane, 1929, 6 1/2 x 9, 114 pages
(Dark blue leather cover with lighter blue embossed lettering)
Ford records indicate about 500 where issued

Parts Price List, Ford Tri-motor Airplane, (5-AT-D Series) 1931, 8 1/2 x 6, 50 pages
Parts Price List, Ford Tri-motor Airplane, (4-AT and 5AT Series) 1932, 8 1/2 x 6,
 74 pages (Both have stiff black covers with silver lettering)

Sales Catalog
The New Era Of Transportation, 1927, 9 x 11, 30 pages
(Light green cover with black printing, string binding)

Now That Man Has Wings, 1928, 9 x 11, 32 pages
(Dark blue with white clouds and light blue airplane)

Now That Man Has Wings, 1929, 9 x 11, 32 pages
(Identical to 1928 catalog except additional page added with new specs)

Promotional book
 Lift Up Your Eyes, 1929, 11 x 14, 42 pages with stiff covers
(Stiff dark blue cover with small silver stars)
Book of 17 aviation ads run by Ford and sent to 1000 influential people.

Literature
Lift Up Your Eyes, c1928, 9 x 7, 6 page foldout, black and white

A Visit To Ford Airport, c1928, 8 1/2 x 4, 4 page foldout, blue and black

Ford All Metal Transport Planes, c1929, 8 1/2 x 11, 4 page foldout, green and black

Now That Everyone Can Fly, c1929, 8 1/2 x 11, 8 pages, blue and black

General Description Ford All-Metal Transport Planes, Jan 1, 1930, 8 1/2 x 11, 12 pages, blue & black

Ford Transport With Packard Diesel Engines, April 1930, 8 1/2 x 11, 4 page foldout, black

No Ford Plane Has Ever Worn Out, c1931, 8 1/2 x 11, 4 page foldout, green and black

Stout Metal Airplane Company literature (Stout owned)

Stout All-metal Airplane, 1925, 8 1/2 x 11, 4 page foldout, black

**Parts Price List
Ford Tri-motor Airplane**

**Book of Instruction
Ford All Metal Monoplane
This book belonged to Harry
Price, top trouble shooter for
Ford's Airplane Division.**

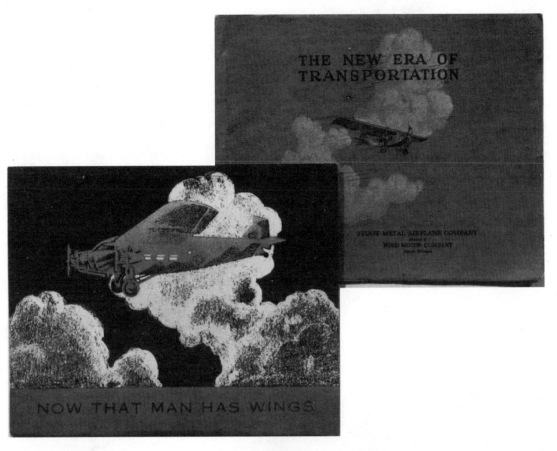

Top, 1927 & 1928 Sales Catalogs.

Right, Ford Airport promotional pamphlet.

Various Ford Tri-motor sales brochures

Significant Dates

1923
Dec 23   Edsel Ford invests in Stout Metal Airplane Company

1924
Apr 23   First flight of *Maiden Detroit* (2AT-1)
Oct 15   Stout occupies factory at Ford Airport

1925
Jan 15   Ford Airport dedicated
Apr 13   Start of Ford Air Transport Service Detroit-to-Chicago
Jul 1   Start of Ford Air Transport Service Detroit-to-Cleveland
Aug 1   Ford purchases 100% of Stout Metal Airplane Company
Sep 28   First Ford Reliability Air Tour starts
Oct 8   First commercial sale of Ford plane. 2AT-7 to John Wanamaker Co
Nov 24   3AT test flight

1926
Jan 17   Fire destroys Stout airplane factory
Feb 15   Start of Ford Airmail flights to Chicago and Cleveland
Jun 11   4AT-1 test flight
Sep 18   US Army airship *RS-1* ties up to mooring mast
Oct 15   US Navy airship *Los Angeles* ties up to mooring mast
Nov   New airplane factory completed

1927
Feb 10   Ford Radio Beacon first used
Apr   Contract let for paving first runway
Jul 21   5AT-1 test flight
Aug 11   Lindbergh takes Henry Ford on first airplane ride
Nov   Airport terminal building opens

1928
Jul 19   Ford terminates Airmail Contracts

1931
Jul 1   Dearborn Inn opens

1932
Aug 6   Ford Air Transport Service terminates

1933
Jun 8   Last Ford Tri-Motor (5AT-116) sold

1935
Nov   Flying wing (15P) built

1941
Nov 11   Ford Air Transportation Office is established

1946
Oct 26   Mooring Mast toppled

1947
Oct 21   Ford Airport closes

William Stout's Association with the Ford Motor Company

1922
Nov 22   William Stout forms the Stout Metal Airplane Company

1923
Dec 21   Edsel Ford invests $2000 in Stout's company

1925
Jul 1   Round Stout medallion used on 2AT-3 (only example known)

Jul 31   Ford purchases the Stout Metal Airplane Company and it becomes:
                The Stout Metal Airplane Company
                Division of Ford Motor Company

1925, continued

Oct 9   First use of the Ford-Stout medallion was on plane sold to the John Wanamaker Co in New York
The Medallion was located on the nose of the airplane on 4AT-1 through 4AT-7 (built 7-26-27) and was located on the side of the fuselage starting with 4AT-8 (10-1-27)

Medallion was used in Ford advertising from first ad August 15, 1927 through December 5, 1927

Nov 24   First Tri-Motor, 3AT, (designed by Stout) test flown

1926

Jan 17   Stout Metal Airplane Company factory burned down with 3AT inside

Aug 1   William Stout forms the Stout Air Service airline with service between Ford Airport and Grand Rapids, MI

1929

Jun   United Aircraft & Transport Corps (forerunner of United Airlines) purchased Stout Air Service

Aug 30   Ford memo regarding proper use of names

Stout Metal Airplane Co, Division of Ford Motor Company
Used in connection with manufacturing and sales of airplanes

Airplane Division of Ford Motor Company
Used in connection with Ford Airport and Ford Air Transport Service

Dec   Last ad to carry Stout name

Dec   All assets of Stout Metal Airplane Company transferred to Ford Motor Company

1930

Mar   William B. Stout leaves Ford Motor Company

1936

Apr 3   Stout Metal Airplane Company Corporations dissolved

List of individuals mentioned in the text

REFERENCES

Ford Industrial Archives, Dearborn, MI

Research Center, Henry Ford Museum and Greenfield Village, Dearborn, MI

Robert Baron papers, Dearborn Historical Society, Dearborn, MI

Robert Baron papers, c/o Michael Erard, Southgate, MI

Stanley Knauss papers, Burton Historical Society, Detroit Public Library, Detroit, MI

Archives, US Postal Service, Washington, DC

National Archives, Washington, DC

Ford News 1924 - 1936, Ford Motor Company employee newsletter

Airship Mooring Tower at Detroit Airport, *Engineering News Record*, February 4, 1926

American Airplane Specifications, *Automotive Industries*, February 18, 1926

Aviation magazine, 1929, series of eight articles by John T. Neville

The New Ford Air Liner, *Aero Digest*, April 1932

Will It Run?, Robert Stewart, *Flying* magazine, May 1943

So Away I Went, William Stout, 1951

My Forty Years With Ford, Charles Sorenson, 1956

Ford: Expansion and Challenge 1915 - 1933, 1957, Allan Nevins & Frank Hill

The Tin Goose, Owen Bombard, May 1958, *Dearborn Historical Quarterly Journal*

A Terror Weapon That Was Never Used, *Detroit News*, November 24, 1961

Ford: Decline and Rebirth 1933 - 1962, 1963, Allan Nevins & Frank Hill

The Wartime Journals of Charles Lindbergh, 1970 Charles Lindbergh

Who Designed The Ford Tri-Motor, *American Aviation Historical Society Journal*, Fall 1970.

The Ford Air Tours, Leslie Forden, 1972

The Tin Bubble, *Air Power* magazine, September 1974

The Secret Life of Henry Ford, John Dahlinger, 1978

History of Ford Air Transportation Department, T. P. Van Sciever, 1980

The Metalclad Airship ZMC 2, Walker Morrow, 1987

Dearborn's Buzz Bomb Engine, Ford Bryan, *The Dearborn Historian*, Winter 1991

Fordair - Europe 1967 - 1992, 1993, Ford Motor Company Ltd.

Willow Run, Don Sherman, *Air & Space* magazine, September 1992

The Ford Tri-Motor 1926 - 1992, William Larkins, 1992

Michigan Aviation: The Early Years, John Bluth, 1993, unpublished manuscript

Flight and Flying, A Chronology, David Baker, 1994

Ford Motor Company and the US Air Mail Service, Tim O'Callaghan, *The Airpost Journal*, April, 1993

Ford Small Experimental Aircraft 1927 - 1936, Tim O'Callaghan, *Skyways* magazine, July 1994

2AT, Before The Ford Tri-Motor, Tim O'Callaghan, *American Aviation Historical Society Journal*, Fall 1994

Engineer's Talent for Design Led to Tri-Motor, Robert Pauley, *The Great Lakes Pilot News,* June/July 1994

4AT-69 after wind storm at Oshkosh, WI in June 1973. Plane was lifted 50 feet in the air and flipped over with disastrous results. The Experimental Aircraft Association purchased the wreck and spent 12 years restoring it. (Hudek)

4AT-69 after restoration in August 1990 on the occasion of the author's first flight. I'm on the left, Paul Poberezny, founder of EAA is on the right. (O'Callaghan)

Ford Motor Company Aviation - Video Tape

In 1963, The Ford Motor Company donated 1.5 million feet of motion picture film taken by their Motion Picture Laboratories to the National Archives. I have had the opportunity of reviewing all of the film relating to Ford's aviation activities and am in the process of editing a 45 to 60 minute video tape. While some of this film had been produced by others, most has never, to my knowledge been offered before. One section is a short film produced by Ford on the opening of their Air Transportation Service between Detroit and Cleveland, while most other parts are pieces fitted together. All footage is from the silent film era. Coverage is planned to include the following items in addition to the above mentioned short film:

> Harry Brooks and the Flivvers
> The Army dirigible *RS-1* at Ford Airport
> The Navy dirigible *Los Angeles* at Ford Airport
> The razing of the Mooring Mast
> Production scenes of the Tri-Motor planes
> Airport and flight scenes of the 2ATs and Tri-Motors
> Charles Lindbergh at Ford Airport

It is anticipated the tape will be available in late 1995 and cost about $32 postpaid. If you are interested, please drop me a post card at the address below. You will be provided with final information on coverage and price when the tape is available.

> T & D Associates
> 46878 Betty Hill
> Plymouth, Michigan 48170